Interactive Mathematics Program®

I M P ™

Integrated High School Mathematics

YEAR 1

The Game of Pig

Dan Fendel and Diane Resek
with
Lynne Alper and Sherry Fraser

Key Curriculum Press
Innovators in Mathematics Education

This material is based upon work
supported by the
National Science Foundation
under award number
ESI-9255262. Any opinions,
findings, and conclusions or
recommendations expressed
in this publication are those of
the authors and do not necessarily
reflect the views of the
National Science Foundation.

®Interactive Mathematics Program is a
registered trademark of Key Curriculum
Press. ™IMP and the IMP logo are
trademarks of Key Curriculum Press.

Key Curriculum Press
1150 65th Street
Emeryville, California 94608
510-595-7000
editorial@keypress.com
http://www.keypress.com

11 10 9 8 7 6 5   03 02 01
ISBN 1-55953-252-1
Printed in the
United States of America

Project Editor
Casey FitzSimons

Additional Editorial Development
Dan Bennett, Bill Finzer, Crystal Mills

Editorial Production
Caroline Ayres, Debbie Cogan,
Greer Lleuad, Jason Luz

Editorial Assistants
Jeff Gammon, Romy Snyder

Teacher Reviews
Dave Calhoun, John Chart, Dwight Fuller,
Donna Gaarder, Dan Johnson, Jean Klanica,
Cathie Thompson

Multicultural Reviews
Edward Castillo, Ph.D., Sonoma State University
Genevieve Lau, Ph.D., Skyline College

Cover and Interior Design
Terry Lockman
Lumina Designworks

Cover Photography and Cover Illustration
Hillary Turner and Tom Fowler

Production
Luis Shein

Production Coordination
Susan Parini

Technical Graphics
Greg Reeves

Illustration
Tom Fowler, Evangelia Philippidis,
Diane Varner, Martha Weston,
April Goodman Willy

Publisher
Steven Rasmussen

Editorial Director
John Bergez

Acknowledgments

Many people have contributed to the development of the IMP™ curriculum, including the hundreds of teachers and many thousands of students who used preliminary versions of the materials. Of course, there is no way to thank all of them individually, but the IMP directors want to give some special acknowledgments.

We want to give extraordinary thanks to the following people who played unique roles in the development of the curriculum.

• **Bill Finzer** was one of the original directors of IMP before going on to different pastures. He helped shape the overall vision of the program, and worked on drafts of several Year 1 units.

• **Matt Bremer** did the initial revision of every unit after its pilot testing. Each unit of the curriculum also underwent extensive focus group reexamination after being taught for several years, and Matt did the rewrite of many units following the focus groups. He has read every word of everyone else's revisions as well, and has contributed tremendous insight through his understanding of high school students and the high school classroom.

• **Mary Jo Cittadino** became a high school student once again during the piloting of the curriculum, attending class daily and doing all the class activities, homework, and POWs. Because of this experience, her contributions to focus groups had a unique perspective. This is a good place to thank her also for her contributions to IMP as Network Coordinator for California. In that capacity, she has visited many IMP classrooms and answered thousands of questions from parents, teachers, and administrators.

• **Lori Green** left the classroom as a regular teacher after the 1989-90 school year and became a traveling resource for IMP classroom teachers. In that role, she has seen more classes using the curriculum than we can count, and the insights from her classroom observations have been a valuable resource in her work in the focus groups.

• **Celia Stevenson** developed the charming and witty graphics that graced the pre-publication versions of all the IMP units.

Several people played particular roles in the development of this unit, *The Game of Pig:*

• Matt Bremer, Janice Bussey, Donna Gaarder, Lori Green, and Tom Zimmerman helped us create the version of *The Game of Pig* that was pilot tested during 1989-90. They not only taught the unit in their classrooms that year, but also read and commented on early drafts, tested out almost all the activities during workshops that preceded the teaching, and then came back after teaching the unit with insights that contributed to the initial revision.

• Janice Bussey, Donna Gaarder, and Steve Jenkins joined Matt Bremer, Mary Jo Cittadino, and Lori Green for the focus group on *The Game of Pig* in June, 1993. Their contributions built on several years of IMP teaching, including at least two years teaching this unit, and their work led to the development of the last field-test version of the unit.

• Dan Branham, Dave Calhoun, John Chart, Steve Hansen, Mary Hunter, Caran Resciniti, Gwennyth Trice, and Julie Walker field tested the post-focus group version of *The Game of Pig* during 1994–95. Dave and John met with us when the teaching of the unit was finished to share their experiences. Their feedback helped shape the final version that now appears.

In creating this program, we needed help in many dimensions other than writing curriculum and giving support to teachers.

The National Science Foundation has been the primary sponsor of the Interactive Mathematics Program®. We want to thank NSF for its ongoing support, and especially want to extend our personal thanks to Dr. Margaret Cozzens, Director of NSF's Division of Elementary, Secondary, and Informal Education, for her encouragement and her faith in our efforts.

We also want to acknowledge here the initial support for curriculum development from the California Postsecondary Education Commission and the San Francisco Foundation, and the major support for dissemination from the Noyce Foundation and the David and Lucile Packard Foundation.

Keeping all of our work going required the help of a first-rate office staff. This group of talented and hard-working individuals worked tirelessly on many tasks, such as sending out units, keeping the books balanced, helping us get our message out to the public, and handling communications with schools, teachers, and administrators. We greatly appreciate their dedication.

• Barbara Ford—Secretary

• Tony Gillies—Project Manager

• Marianne Smith—Publicist

• Linda Witnov—Outreach Coordinator

We want to thank Dr. Norman Webb, of the Wisconsin Center for Education Research, for his leadership in our evaluation program, and our Evaluation Advisory Board, whose expertise was so valuable in that aspect of our work.

• David Clarke, University of Melbourne

• Robert Davis, Rutgers University

• George Hein, Lesley College

• Mark St. John, Inverness Research Associates

Finally, we want to thank Steve Rasmussen, President of Key Curriculum Press, Casey FitzSimons, Key's Project Editor for the IMP curriculum, and the many others at Key whose work turned our ideas and words into published form.

Dan Fendel   Diane Resek   Lynne Alper   Sherry Fraser

The Interactive Mathematics Program

What is the Interactive Mathematics Program?

The Interactive Mathematics Program (IMP) is a growing collaboration of mathematicians, teacher-educators, and teachers who have been working together since 1989 on both curriculum development and teacher professional development.

What is the IMP curriculum?

IMP has created a four-year program of problem-based mathematics that replaces the traditional Algebra I–Geometry–Algebra II/Trigonometry–Precalculus sequence and that is designed to exemplify the curriculum reform called for in the *Curriculum and Evaluation Standards* of the National Council of Teachers of Mathematics.

The IMP curriculum integrates traditional material with additional topics recommended by the NCTM *Standards*, such as statistics, probability, curve fitting, and matrix algebra. Although every IMP unit has a specific mathematical focus (for instance, similar triangles), most units are structured around a central problem and bring in other topics as needed to solve that problem, rather than narrowly restricting the mathematical content. Ideas that are developed in one unit are generally revisited and deepened in one or more later units.

For which students is the IMP curriculum intended?

The IMP curriculum is for all students. One of IMP's goals is to make the learning of a core mathematics curriculum accessible to everyone. Toward that end, we have designed the program for use with heterogeneous classes. We provide you with a varied collection of supplemental problems to give you the flexibility to meet individual student needs.

Teacher Phyllis Quick confers with a group of students.

How is the IMP classroom different?

When you use the IMP curriculum, your role changes from "imparter of knowledge" to observer and facilitator. You ask challenging questions. You do not give all the answers but you prod students to do their own thinking, to make generalizations, and to go beyond the immediate problem by asking themselves "What if?"

The IMP curriculum gives students many opportunities to write about their mathematical thinking, to reflect on what they have done, and to make oral presentations to each other about their work. In IMP, your assessment of students becomes integrated with learning, and you evaluate students in a variety of ways, including class participation, daily homework assignments, Problems of the Week, portfolios, and unit assessments. The IMP *Teaching Handbook* provides many practical suggestions for teachers on how to get the best possible results using this curriculum in *your* classroom.

What is in Year 1 of the IMP curriculum?

Year 1 of the IMP curriculum contains five units.

Patterns

The primary purpose of this unit is to introduce students to ways of working on and thinking about mathematics that may be new to them. In a sense, the unit is an overall introduction to the IMP curriculum, which involves changes for many students in how they learn mathematics and what they think of as mathematics. The main mathematical ideas of the unit include function tables, the use of variables, positive and negative numbers, and some basic geometrical concepts.

The Game of Pig

A dice game called Pig forms the core of this unit. Playing and analyzing Pig involves students in a wide variety of mathematical activities. The basic problem for students is to find an optimum strategy for playing the game. In order to find a good strategy and prove that it is optimum, students work with the concept of expected value and develop a mathematical analysis for the game based on an area model for probability.

The Overland Trail

This unit looks at the mid-nineteenth century western migration across what is now the United States in terms of the many mathematical relationships involved. These relationships involve planning what to take on the 2400-mile trek, estimating the cost of the move, studying rates of consumption and of travel, and estimating the time to reach the final goal. A major mathematical focus of the unit is the use of equations, tables, and graphs to describe real-life situations.

The Pit and the Pendulum

In Edgar Allan Poe's story, *The Pit and the Pendulum,* a prisoner is tied down while a pendulum with a sharp blade slowly descends. If the prisoner does not act, he will be killed by the pendulum. Students read an excerpt from the story, and are presented with the problem of whether the prisoner would have enough time to escape. To resolve this question, they construct pendulums and conduct experiments. In the process, they are introduced to the concepts of normal distribution and standard deviation as tools for determining whether a change in one variable really does affect another. They use graphing calculators to learn about quadratic equations and to explore curve fitting. Finally, after deriving a theoretical answer to the pendulum problem, students actually build a thirty-foot pendulum to test their theory.

Shadows

The central question of this unit is, "How can you predict the length of a shadow?" The unit moves quickly from this concrete problem to the geometric concept of similarity. Students work with a variety of approaches to come to an understanding of similar polygons, especially similar triangles. Then they return to the problem of the shadow, applying their knowledge of similar triangles and using informal methods for solving proportions, to develop a general formula. In the last part of the unit, students learn about the three primary trigonometric functions—sine, cosine, and tangent— as they apply to acute angles, and they apply these functions to problems of finding heights and distances.

How do the four years of the IMP curriculum fit together?

The four years of the IMP curriculum form an integrated sequence through which students can learn the mathematics they will need, both for further education and on the job. Although the organization of the IMP curriculum is very different from the traditional Algebra I–Geometry–Algebra II/Trigonometry–Precalculus sequence, the important mathematical ideas are all there.

Here are some examples of how both traditional concepts and topics new to the high school curriculum are developed.

Linear equations

In Year 1 of the IMP curriculum, students develop an intuitive foundation about algebraic thinking, including the use of variables, which they build on throughout the program. In the Year 2 unit *Solve It!,* students use the concept of equivalent equations to see how to solve any linear equation in a single variable. Later in Year 2, in a unit called *Cookies* (about maximizing profits for a bakery), they solve pairs of linear equations in two variables, using both algebraic and geometric methods. In the Year 3 unit *Meadows or Malls?,* they extend those ideas to systems with more than two variables, and see how to use matrices and the technology of graphing calculators to solve such systems.

Measurement and the Pythagorean theorem

Measurement, including area and volume, is one of the fundamental topics in geometry. The Pythagorean theorem is one of the most important geometric principles ever discovered. In the Year 2 unit *Do Bees Build It Best?*, students combine these ideas with their knowledge of similarity (from the Year 1 unit *Shadows*) to see why the hexagonal prism of the bees' honeycomb design is the most efficient regular prism possible. Students also use the Pythagorean theorem in later units, applying it to develop principles like the distance formula in coordinate geometry.

Trigonometric functions

In traditional programs, the trigonometric functions are introduced in the eleventh or twelfth grade. In the IMP curriculum, students begin working with trigonometry in Year 1 (in *Shadows*), using right-triangle trigonometry in several units (including *Do Bees Build It Best?*) in Years 2 and 3. In the Year 4 unit *High Dive,* they extend trigonometry from right triangles to circular functions, in the context of a circus act in which a performer falls from a Ferris wheel into a moving tub of water. (In *High Dive,* students also learn principles of physics, developing laws for falling objects and finding the vertical and horizontal components of velocity.)

Standard deviation and the binomial distribution

Standard deviation and the binomial distribution are major tools in the study of probability and statistics. *The Game of Pig* gets students started by building a firm understanding of concepts of probability and the phenomenon of experimental variation. Later in Year 1 (in *The Pit and the Pendulum*), they use standard deviation to see that the period of a pendulum is determined primarily by its length. In Year 2, they compare standard deviation with the chi-square test in examining whether a set of data is statistically significant. In *Pennant Fever* (Year 3), students use the binomial distribution to evaluate a team's chances of winning the baseball championship, and in *The Pollster's Dilemma* (Year 4), students tie many of these ideas together in the central limit theorem, seeing how the margin of error and the level of certainty for an election poll depend on its size.

Does the program work?

The IMP curriculum has been thoroughly field-tested by hundreds of classroom teachers around the country. Their enthusiasm comes from the success they have seen in their own classrooms with their own students. For those who measure success by test scores, we mention that repeated studies have proved that IMP students do at least as well as students in traditional mathematics classes on tests like the SAT, even though IMP students spend far less time than traditional students on the algebra and geometry skills emphasized by these tests. With the time saved, IMP students learn topics such as statistics that other students don't see until they reach college.

But one of our proudest achievements is that IMP students are excited about mathematics, as shown by the fact that they take more mathematics courses in high school than their counterparts in traditional programs. We think this is because they see that mathematics can be relevant to their own lives. If so, then the program works.

Dan Fendel
Diane Resek
Lynne Alper
Sherry Fraser

Note to Students

These pages in the student book welcome students to the program.

You are about to begin an adventure in mathematics, an adventure organized around interesting, complex problems. The concepts you learn grow out of what is needed to solve those problems.

This curriculum was developed by the Interactive Mathematics Program (IMP), a collaboration of teachers, teacher-educators, and mathematicians who have been working together since 1989 to reform the way high school mathematics is taught. About one hundred thousand students and five hundred teachers used these materials before they were published. Their experiences, reactions, and ideas have been incorporated into the final version you now hold.

Our goal is to give you the mathematics you need to succeed in this changing world. We want to present mathematics to you in a manner that reflects how mathematics is used and reflects the different ways people work and learn together. Through this perspective on mathematics, you will be prepared both for continued study of mathematics in college and for the world of work.

This book contains the various assignments that will be your work during Year 1 of the program. As you will see, these assignments incorporate ideas from many branches of mathematics, including algebra, geometry, probability, graphing, statistics, and trigonometry. Other topics will come up in later parts of this four-year program. Rather than present each of these areas separately, we have integrated them and presented them in meaningful contexts so that you'll see how they relate to one another and to our world.

Each unit in this four-year program has a central problem or theme, and focuses on several major mathematical ideas. Within each unit, the material is organized for teaching purposes into "Days," with a homework assignment for each day. (Your class may not follow this schedule exactly, especially if it doesn't meet every day.)

At the end of the main material for each unit, you will find a set of "supplemental problems." These problems provide additional opportunities for you to work with ideas from the unit, either to strengthen your understanding of the core material or to explore new ideas related to the unit.

Although the IMP program is not organized into courses called Algebra, Geometry, and so on, you will be learning all the essential mathematical concepts that are part of those traditional courses. You will also be learning concepts from branches of mathematics—especially statistics and probability—that are not part of a traditional high school program.

To accomplish this goal, you will have to be an active learner. Simply reading this book will not allow you to achieve your goal, because the book does not teach directly. Your role as a mathematics student will be to experiment, investigate, ask questions, make and test conjectures, and reflect, and then communicate your ideas and conclusions both verbally and in writing. You will do some work in collaboration with your fellow students, just as users of mathematics in the real world often work in teams. At other times, you will be working on your own.

We hope you will enjoy the challenge of this new way of learning mathematics and will see mathematics in a new light.

Dan Fendel   Diane Resek   Lynne Alper   Sherry Fraser

Finding What You Need

We designed this guide to help you find what you need amid all the information it provides. Each of the following components has a special treatment in the layout of the guide.

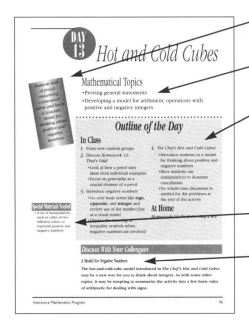

Synopsis of the Day: The key idea or activity for each day is summarized in a brief sentence or two.

Mathematical Topics: Mathematical issues for the day are presented in a bulleted list.

Outline of the Day: Under the *In Class* heading, the outline summarizes the activities for the day, which are keyed to numbered headings in the discussion. Daily homework assignments and Problems of the Week are listed under the *At Home* heading.

Special Materials Needed: Special items needed in the classroom for each day are bulleted here.

Discuss With Your Colleagues: This section highlights topics that you may want to discuss with your peers.

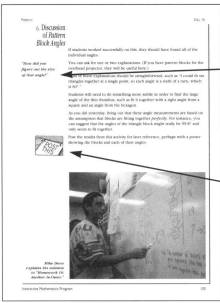

Suggested Questions: These are specific questions that you might ask during an activity or discussion to promote student insight or to determine whether students understand an idea. The appropriateness of these questions generally depends on what students have already developed or presented on their own.

Post This: The *Post This* icon indicates items that you may want to display in the classroom.

Icons for Student Written Products

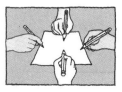

Single Group report

Individual reports

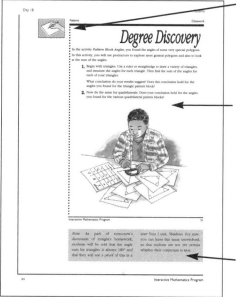

Icons for Student Written Products: For each group activity, there is an icon suggesting a single group report, individual reports, or no report at all. If graphs are included, the icon indicates this as well. (The graph icons do not appear in every unit.)

Embedded Student Pages: Embedded within the pages of the teacher guide are reduced-size copies of the pages from the student book. These reduced student pages include the "transition pages" that appear occasionally within each unit to summarize each portion of the unit and to prepare students for what is coming. Having all of these student pages in the teacher guide is a helpful way for you to see things from the students' perspective.

Asides: These are ideas outside the main thrust of a discussion. They include background information for teachers, refinements or subtle points that may only be of interest to some students, ways to help fill in gaps in understanding the main ideas, and suggestions about when to bring in a particular concept.

Additional Information

Here is a brief outline of other tools we have included to assist you and make both the teaching and the learning experience more rewarding.

Glossary: This section, which is found at the back of the book, gives the definitions of important terms for all of Year 1 for easy reference. The same glossary appears in the student book.

Appendix A: Supplemental Problems: This appendix contains a variety of interesting additional activities for the unit, for teachers who would like to supplement material found in the regular classroom problems. These additional activities are of two types—*reinforcements,* which help increase student understanding of concepts that are central to the unit, and *extensions,* which allow students to explore ideas beyond the basic unit.

Appendix B: Blackline Masters: For each unit, this appendix contains materials you can reproduce that are not available in the student book and that will be helpful to teacher and student alike. They include the end-of-unit assessments as well as such items as diagrams from which you can make transparencies. Semester assessments for Year 1 are included in *The Overland Trail* (for first semester) and *Shadows* (for second semester).

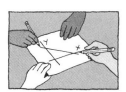

Single group graph

Individual graphs

No report at all

Year 1 IMP Units

Patterns

The Game of Pig (in this book)

The Overland Trail

The Pit and the Pendulum

Shadows

Contents

"The Game of Pig" Overview

Summary of the Unit

A dice game called Pig forms the core of this unit. Playing and analyzing Pig involves students in a wide variety of mathematical activities. The basic problem facing students is to find an optimum strategy for playing the game. In order to find a good strategy and prove that it is optimum, students work with the concept of expected value—the average in the long run—and develop mathematical models for the game based on area diagrams.

Probabilistic thinking frequently runs counter to our intuitions, and, for this reason, the activities in this unit are based in concrete experiences. Students' beliefs in luck are terribly persistent, and it often takes a great deal of experience before they become willing to base their predictions on probabilistic notions. The gambler's fallacy—that the next roll of the dice depends on previous rolls—is held with conviction even by well-informed adults. One goal of this unit is to have students recognize this fallacy, both in dice games and in real-life situations.

As an introduction to the various concepts and skills needed to analyze Pig, students work on a number of other problems, including "rug problems" (which introduce the area model for probability), spinner problems, and problems involving free throws in basketball and alternative payment plans for a newspaper carrier. Tree diagrams are used as a technique for listing or organizing sequences of events.

Through these problems, students develop the concept of expected value and learn to calculate expected value using an area model. Then students encounter some real-life "games," such as buying insurance and playing the lottery, and see that these are situations where expected value is not the sole criterion for making a decision.

Near the end of the unit, students study a simplified version of Pig, called Little Pig. They can find the expected value for various strategies for this game by using an area model. By comparing the analyses for different strategies, they are able to develop a general analysis that allows them to find the best strategy for Little Pig.

They then apply this general analysis to find the best strategy for the Pig game itself. As an option, students may use computer simulations of Little Pig and Pig to see whether the theoretical results they have found are borne out over a large number of trials.

Problems of the Week in this unit involve concepts of probability and strategy. In the final POW of the unit, students use these concepts to create their own game.

Here is a summary showing the overall organization of the unit.

- Days 1–2: Introduction to the game of Pig

- Days 3–11: Basic concepts of probability, including independent events, theoretical versus observed probability, and use of an area model

- Days 12–20: Introduction of expected value, using spinners and "pointed rugs"; use of expected value in a variety of situations; use of random number generator; tree diagrams

- Day 21: Writing a calculator program to do a probability simulation

- Days 22–26: Introduction of Little Pig; using area diagrams to analyze strategies for Little Pig; finding the best strategy for Little Pig and running a computer simulation

- Day 27: Finding the best strategy for Pig and running a computer simulation

- Days 28–32: Work on POW 7, portfolios, and end-of-unit assessments; summing up; sharing POW 7 games

Concepts and Skills

The main concepts and skills that students will encounter and practice during the course of this unit can be summarized by category as shown below.

Strategies

- Learning what constitutes a "complete strategy"

- Developing and analyzing strategies

Probability

- Expressing probability as a number between zero and one

- Calculating probabilities based on equally likely events and area models

- Deciding whether events are independent

- Using "the long run" to develop the concept of expected value

- Calculating and interpreting expected values

- Solving problems involving conditional probability

- Extending a probabilistic analysis from a simple situation to a similar but more complex one

Representations of probability

- Constructing mathematical models, particularly area models, for probabilistic situations
- Creating situations that fit a given probabilistic model
- Making and interpreting frequency bar graphs

Simulations

- Using simulations to estimate probabilities
- Comparing the theoretical analysis of a situation with experimental results
- Seeing how the number of trials in a simulation affects the results
- Writing a calculator program to create a simulation
- Using a computer simulation to compare strategies

Probability in the Interactive Mathematics Program

This unit is written on the assumption that it will be most students' first serious exposure to concepts of probability.

You will need to gauge your students' level of preparation in the early days of the unit, and adjust the pace and your expectations accordingly. The unit deals with some fundamental and profound ideas, and students' appreciation of these ideas will develop gradually throughout the curriculum of the Interactive Mathematics Program.

The unit emphasizes building an intuitive foundation, rather than learning computational rules. Students can build on that foundation in future units, using this work on probability to establish sophisticated concepts from statistics. Concepts of probability and statistics also play a major role in these IMP units:

- *The Pit and the Pendulum* (Year 1)
- *Is There Really a Difference?* (Year 2)
- *Pennant Fever* (Year 3)
- *The Pollster's Dilemma* (Year 4)

Materials

You will need to provide these materials during the course of the unit (in addition to standard materials such as graphing calculators, transparencies, chart paper, marking pens, and so forth):

- Dice (one pair, of different colors, per student)
- At least three red, two blue, and two yellow colored cubes (or similar materials) per pair of students

- Paper bags (from which to pick cubes)

- Sentence strips (strips of paper roughly 6′ by 3′) for posting important principles or results

- Computer and *IMP Pig* computer software, available on the publisher's World Wide Web site

- Overhead viewer for computer

Grading

The IMP *Teaching Handbook* contains general ideas about how to grade students in an IMP class. You will probably want to check daily that students have done their homework, and include the regular completion of homework as part of students' grades. Your grading scheme will probably include Problems of the Week, the unit portfolio, and the end-of-unit assessments.

Because you will not be able to read thoroughly every assignment that students turn in, you will need to select certain assignments to read carefully and to base grades on. Here are some suggestions:

- *Pig Strategies* (Day 2 activity)

- *Homework 6: 0 to 1, or Never to Always*

- *Homework 11: Two-Dice Sums and Products*

- *Spinner Give and Take* (Day 12 activity)

- *Spins and Draws* (Day 17 activity)

- *Homework 20: A Fair Deal for the Carrier?*

- *Little Pig Strategies* (Day 23 activity) or *The Best Little Pig* (Day 26 activity)

- *Homework 27: The Pig and I*

If you want to base your grading on more tasks, there are many other homework assignments, class activities, and oral presentations you can use.

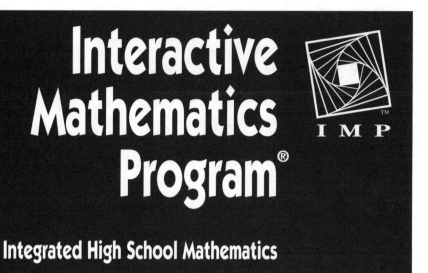

Interactive Mathematics Program®

IMP

Integrated High School Mathematics

YEAR 1

The Game of Pig

The Game of Pig

**Days
1-2**

A Game of Chance and Strategy

The theory of probability was developed in the seventeenth century, primarily to answer questions posed by gamblers. Mathematicians of the time saw that strategies can be developed to optimize the chances of success, even in situations involving luck. Today, probability is used in a variety of applications, ranging from scientific research to making practical business decisions.

In *The Game of Pig* you'll explore the world of probability with a dice game called Pig. In the opening days of this unit, you'll experiment as the first step toward finding the best strategy for the game.

*This page in the
student book
introduces Days 1
and 2.*

*Leah Allen and
Crystal Kovarik
begin the unit by
playing the game
of Pig in order to
develop the best
strategy.*

Interactive Mathematics Program   95

DAY 1 — The Game of Pig

Students learn the game of Pig and begin to think about strategy.

Mathematical Topics

- Introducing the game of Pig
- The meaning of "strategy"
- Developing strategies for the game of Pig

Outline of the Day

In Class

1. Form new random groups
2. Discuss the idea of a central unit problem
3. *The Game of Pig*
   - Introduce students to the game
   - Talk informally about the meaning of the term "strategy"
   - Students play in groups and think about possible strategies
4. Discuss *The Game of Pig*
   - Have students share experiences
   - Begin to examine the question of how to compare strategies

At Home

Homework 1: Pig at Home

POW 4: A Sticky Gum Problem (due Day 8)

Special Materials Needed

- A die for each pair of students

Note: Although *POW 4: A Sticky Gum Problem* is included in today's discussion, you may prefer to wait until tomorrow to introduce it to the class, perhaps asking students just to read the problem as part of tonight's homework.

1. Form Groups

At the beginning of the unit, put students into new groups as described in the IMP *Teaching Handbook*. We recommend that new groups be formed again on Day 10 and on Day 19.

2. The Idea of a Unit Problem

This unit is the first that involves students in a long-term study of a single problem. You may want to talk to the class about the idea of starting with a complex problem that they may not solve for many weeks, and tell them that most of the four-year IMP curriculum is organized this way.

Interactive Mathematics Program

3

• *Note: Social issues concerning dice and gambling*

Some students and parents may be concerned about school activities that involve dice or seem to involve gambling. You may need to discuss this issue with students directly.

Although the theory of probability has its origins largely in the study of gambling, the concepts are used in many fields, including the natural sciences and the social sciences. We use dice rolling and coin flipping in the curriculum because they provide simple models for studying complex ideas about probability.

The study of statistics is based on ideas of probability, and students will be studying and using statistics throughout the curriculum. People make decisions every day based on intuitive conceptions and misconceptions about probability and statistics, and one of the goals of this unit is to help students become better decision-makers. Activities such as *The Gambler's Fallacy* (Day 3) and *Homework 18: The Lottery and Insurance—Why Play?* are intended to help students with the social dimensions of probability.

You may find it preferable to refer to dice as "probability cubes" or "random number generators." (On Day 18, students will use the random number generator on their calculators, which gives them decimals between 0 and 1, rather than whole numbers from 1 to 6.)

3. *The Game of Pig*
(see facing page)

Have students turn to the activity *The Game of Pig* and read the instructions for the game. (You may want to ask different students to read portions of the instructions out loud.)

Although the activity does not state any specific goal, students will generally assume that, in some sense, they are to get as many points as possible. The task of the unit will be defined more precisely tomorrow.

Play a few turns with the class as a whole to clarify the rules. It is natural for there to be some confusion as to exactly how to play the game. In particular, be sure that the class distinguishes between a single roll of the die and a turn.

Then have students play the game for a while within their groups, first as a whole group and then in pairs (Questions 1 and 2 of the activity). As they work, you can make sure that they understand how the game is played.

• *The meaning of "strategy"*

"What do you think a strategy is?"

Before asking students to explore different strategies for Pig (Question 3 of the activity), ask students to describe what they think a strategy is.

"How do you use strategies in your daily life?"

You can ask students how they use strategies on an everyday basis in their lives, or where strategies are used. For example, there are military strategies, sports strategies, and even studying strategies. For instance, a person might devise a strategy for studying for several tests on a single day.

The Game of Pig

The Game

To play this game, you need an ordinary six-sided die, labeled 1 through 6.

Each turn of the game consists of one or more rolls of the die. You keep rolling until you decide to stop or until you roll 1. You may choose to stop rolling at any time.

Continued on next page

Emphasize that in *mathematics,* a strategy is a *complete plan of action,* usually intended to reach some goal. To be a strategy for Pig, a plan must tell you whether or not to roll again, in *every* circumstance in which you have a choice.

Tell students that when they write a strategy for Pig, someone should be able to follow the instructions *without having to make any independent decisions.* It may help to say that a robot or a computer should be able to carry out the strategy.

Scoring

If you choose to stop rolling *before* you roll 1, your score for that turn is the sum of all the numbers you rolled on that turn.

However, if you roll 1, your turn is over, and your score for that turn is 0.

Examples

- You roll 4, 5, and 2, and then decide to stop. Your score for this turn is 11.

- You roll 3, 4, 6, and 1. The turn is over because you rolled 1, and your score for this turn is 0.

Each turn is scored separately. With each turn you play, you add the score for that turn to the total of your previous turns.

Your Assignment

1. Play several turns as a whole group. As you play, talk about how you are deciding whether or not to roll again.

2. Split into two smaller groups and play some more turns.

3. Make a list of some strategies that you found yourselves using. Be prepared to discuss these with the entire class.

For example, "Roll again if your last roll was an even number, and stop if your last roll was an odd number" is a complete strategy. (This may not be a very good plan, but it is complete.) On the other hand, the plan "Roll at least twice" is not a complete strategy, since it doesn't tell you whether or not to continue after two rolls. Also, "If you feel lucky, then roll again" is not a strategy, since feelings change from person to person, and so these instructions are ambiguous.

• *Trying Pig strategies*

After the discussion of what a strategy is, let students spend a while playing the game and experimenting with different strategies. As you circulate, get students to write down their strategies as clearly as possible.

4. Discussion of *The Game of Pig*

"Describe some of the strategies you used. How did you decide whether to roll again or to stop?"

After students have had a while to play the game, ask them to discuss their experiences. You do not need to get a list of all the strategies used, but you should get students to describe at least a couple. The basic problem in defining a strategy is deciding when to roll again to get more points for a given turn, and when to stop on a given turn and not risk losing one's points.

Here are some further questions you might ask.

• What were some high scores for individual turns?

• How did your strategy change as you played Pig and understood the game better?

> Students will work more on articulating strategies in the discussion of tomorrow's activity, *Pig Strategies*.

• *Comparing strategies*

"How might you measure whether one strategy is any better than another?"

As yet, no clear idea has been given to students as to what their goal is. You can get them started on this process by posing this question.

> *How might you measure whether one strategy is any better than another?*

Work with students' responses, but move them toward a consideration of what happens "in the long run." This is a key idea throughout the unit, and students will probably only gradually grasp its implications. But it is important to start talking about this now. (We will define "best strategy" more precisely tomorrow.)

For example, students should understand that it is better to score 15 points on each of two turns than to score 25 points on one turn and no points on the other. If necessary, clarify that they are not playing turn by turn against another player, so there is never a need to beat a particular score.

> *Note: POW 5: What's on Back?* and *POW 6: Linear Nim* will give students the opportunity to explore concepts of strategy in two other contexts.

Homework 1: *Pig at Home*
(see next page)

The purpose of this homework is to make students more comfortable with the game and to get them to give more thought to strategies.

Homework 1   Pig at Home

Play Pig with someone at home. If you don't have a die, you can put numbers on a wooden cube, or you can write the numbers 1 through 6 on cards and put them in a bag. If you use cards, mix the bag well each time before drawing out a card, and replace the card after each draw.

Then write about your experience playing Pig. Include in your write-up:

- Who you played with

- How you taught them to play

- What strategies each of you used and which seemed most effective

- Whether you played "with each other" or "against each other," and why

Students will find it easier to do some of the homework assignments in this unit if they have dice at home. You may choose to lend dice to students for the duration of the unit if they have a problem obtaining their own at home.

This assignment suggests some homemade alternatives to dice that students might use, although such alternatives may be cumbersome in later assignments.

POW 4 *A Sticky Gum Problem*

This Problem of the Week starts with some specific problems, and then asks you to generalize what you've learned from them.

Here's the first problem.

1. Ms. Hernandez comes across a gum ball machine one day when she is out with her twins. Of course, the twins each want a gum ball. What's more, they insist on being given gum balls of the same color. (They don't care what color the gum balls are, as long as they're the same color.)

   Ms. Hernandez can see that there are only white gum balls and red gum balls in the machine. The gum balls are a penny each, and there is no way to tell which color will come out next. Ms. Hernandez decides she will keep putting in pennies until she gets two gum balls of the same color.

   Why is three cents the most she might have to spend in order to satisfy her twins?

The next two problems are similar to Question 1.

2. The next day, Ms. Hernandez passes a different gum ball machine. This one has three colors—red, white, and blue.

   What is the most Ms. Hernandez might have to spend at this new gum ball machine in order to get matching gum balls for her twins?

Continued on next page

POW 4: A Sticky Gum Problem

> *Reminder:* As indicated in the outline for today, you may prefer to introduce this POW on Day 2, and just have students look it over tonight as part of their homework.

Have students look at *POW 4: A Sticky Gum Problem*. You might want to discuss the answer to the first gum ball question right away, so you can be sure that all students understand the nature of the questions.

3. Here comes Mr. Hodges with his triplets past the three-color gum ball machine described in Question 2. Of course, his children also insist that they all get the same color gum ball. What is the most Mr. Hodges might have to spend?

After you have answered the questions above, create some examples of your own. You may want to begin with more examples about the Hernandez twins, using different numbers of colors. Or you may want to create other examples using the three-color gum ball machine and larger sets of children.

As you create and solve examples of your own, look for a way to organize the information and look for patterns. Your ultimate goal is to find a formula so that, if someone tells you the number of colors and the number of children, your formula will tell you the maximum that the parent might need to spend.

Write-up

Your write-up for this Problem of the Week should begin with a discussion of Questions 1 through 3. Explain your answers to each of these problems and describe the process by which you solved them.

Then discuss the problems you made up and their solutions. Explain how you organized your information and what patterns you found.

Finally, state any general ideas you were able to formulate. Include conjectures you may have about the general problem, even if you can't prove them. For each general statement, include an explanation of why you think it's true and examples to illustrate it, as well as a description of the process by which you arrived at the idea.

Adapted from "A Sticky Gum Problem" in *aha! Insight* by Martin Gardner, W. H. Freeman and Company, New York City/San Francisco, 1978.

● ●

Also, you may want to point out that the write-up does not use the usual categories, but still calls on students to explain their thinking.

Presentations for this POW are scheduled for Day 8. You can remind the class that three students who have not yet made POW presentations will be randomly selected the day before the problem is due.

Pig Strategies

Mathematical Topics

- Evaluating different strategies for Pig
- Defining "best strategy"

Outline of the Day

In Class

1. Discuss *Homework 1: Pig at Home*
2. *Pig Strategies*
   - Students share strategies and choose one that they think is best
3. Discuss *Pig Strategies*
   - Define "best strategy" as *highest average per turn in the long run*

- Post each group's proposed strategy
- Post the unit goal

At Home

Homework 2: Waiting for a Double

Special Materials Needed

- A die for each group of students

Discuss With Your Colleagues

The "Long Run"

"In the long run" and "the best strategy" are concepts that are probably somewhat hazy now to your students. These ideas will gradually become clearer over the course of the unit. It is important to let these ideas develop in a way that allows students to really absorb them.

How can teachers support each other in the psychological transition from a curriculum based on the mastery of mechanics to a curriculum based on an understanding of ideas?

1. Discussion of *Homework 1: Pig at Home*

Students will be sharing their strategies in groups as part of today's activity, *Pig Strategies,* so you need not spend time discussing the strategies. However, you may want to ask students if they had any particular experiences that they wish to share, perhaps asking them to focus on how the person at home reacted to being involved with the problem.

You may also wish to inquire whether students had difficulty obtaining dice or what alternatives they used.

2. *Pig Strategies*
(see next page)

Tell students that today's activity focuses on the meaning of strategy and on the need for clarity when one wants to communicate a strategy—that is, a complete plan—to another person.

Go over the different parts of the *Pig Strategies* activity with the class, and emphasize that each group must create a complete, written strategy for another group to use. You can have each group put its strategy on a sentence strip, for display during the discussion.

While students work on this activity, you can get a sense of how they are thinking about strategies.

3. Discussion of *Pig Strategies*

Have the club card student in each group hold up the sentence strip with the group's "best strategy" and read it to the class.

"Does that group's strategy seem complete and clear?"

Ask the class if the strategy seems complete and if it is clear enough. Encourage students to challenge each other's ideas (constructively), with comments such as "Your strategy doesn't tell me what to do if . . . ." The presenting group should clarify any ambiguities and change their written strategy if needed. You can also ask the presenters to talk about the difficulties they encountered in trying to write down their strategies.

When the class decides that a group's strategy is clear, have the group post it for reference. If possible, keep these strategies posted until the unit has ended.

When every group has a clear strategy, let them try various groups' strategies (including their own, if they wish). Each group should play ten turns with each strategy they try, record their score for each turn, and find their total

Pig Strategies

Continue working in your groups on developing strategies for Pig.

1. Share with group members the strategies you each used in *Homework 1: Pig at Home*.

2. Discuss these strategies, and decide on the strategy you think is the best that you have found so far. (It may be one of those written for homework, or it may be something new.)

3. Write this "best strategy" in such a way that another group would be able to play Pig using this strategy.

Interactive Mathematics Program   101

score for the ten turns. (Some individual turns will have scores of zero.)

• *What do we mean by "best strategy"?*

"What do we really mean by 'the best strategy'?"

When the discussion and experimentation is completed, continue yesterday's discussion by asking students "What do we really mean by 'the best strategy'?"

As already noted, the activity, *The Game of Pig,* does not define a specific goal, so you may need to lead the class in making the goal precise. In this unit, "best" will mean *highest average per turn in the long run*. On Day 14, students will learn the formal name, *expected value,* for this concept, but meanwhile you can begin to focus students' attention on the idea of average score.

"Consider the following results . . . Which player seems to have used the better strategy?"

One way to begin is with some comparisons. For example, ask students to imagine two players using different strategies. One player has played 500 turns and scored 1185 points; the other has played 600 turns and scored 1342 points.

Ask students to think about which player seems to have used the better strategy, and to try to come to a consensus in their groups about this. Then let some volunteers present their groups' decisions and reasons.

As needed, bring out that at the rate the players are going, when each player has played 1000 turns (or any other particular number), the first player will have more points than the second, since the first player has a higher *average per turn*.

• Setting the unit task

After an example or two like this, you can tell students that, for this unit, "best" will mean "most points per turn in the long run," and that their central task in the unit will be to find the best strategy for Pig.

You should post this goal for reference during the course of the unit.

Unit Goal   **To find the strategy for Pig that gives the most points per turn in the long run.**

You should make clear that finding the best strategy is not an easy task, and certainly not one that they are expected to be able to do right away. Tell students that they gradually will be building up ideas that will help them accomplish this task, and they will spend some time on related problems in order to develop the necessary concepts.

> *Note:* Since Pig is a game of chance, there is no guarantee that the best strategy will give the highest score in any given set of games. You may want to clarify that the best strategy is the one that is most likely to win in the long run.

Homework 2: Waiting for a Double
(see facing page)

You may want to introduce the homework assignment by rolling a pair of dice in front of the class until you get a double, to ensure that students understand what is being counted.

Homework 2   Waiting for a Double

In many games that use dice, such as backgammon, you roll two dice at a time. Often special rules apply when you roll a double. (A **double** means having the same number show on both dice).

So you might want to know how long it takes to get a double. Here is an experiment to consider.

> You roll a pair of dice, and continue rolling until you get a double. You record the number of rolls it took to get a double.

Example:

First roll	Dice come up 3 and 4.
Second roll	Dice come up 2 and 5.
Third roll	Dice come up 5 and 3.
Fourth roll	Dice come up 2 and 2.

It took four rolls to get a double.

Continued on next page

Also, if you think they need to review how to compute an average, you may want to ask students to explain how they will compute the average that is asked for in Question 3. You may wish to have them work through an example with sample numbers.

1. Predict the *average* number of rolls it will take to get a double. Write a sentence or two explaining why you made that prediction.

2. Do the experiment ten times. That is, for each experiment, roll a pair of dice until you get a double, counting how many rolls it takes. Write down the number of rolls needed each time.

3. Use the data you gathered in Question 2 to answer these questions.

    a. What was the largest number of rolls it took to get a double? What was the smallest?

    b. What was the average of the ten experiments?

4. How close is the average you found in Question 3b to the prediction you made in Question 1? Would you revise your prediction now, based on your experiments? Why or why not?

• *The importance of genuine data*

"Why is it important to get genuine data on activities like this?"

Finally, lead a discussion with students on the importance of getting genuine data on activities like this. Tell them that they will be drawing conclusions based on their data, and if they "fake" the data, it might lead to misconceptions.

Point out also that, just as they should not make up a data set that "seems right," neither should they discard data that they get from an experiment just because it "seems weird."

Make it clear that, if for some reason, a student cannot find the time to do the experiment, the student should report that fact and not copy someone else's data.

Days 3-6

Flip, Flip

This page in the student book introduces Days 3 through 6.

You've seen that the game of Pig is rather complicated. Although you may already have a favorite strategy, you're still a long way from completely understanding the game. That understanding probably won't come until the end of this unit. To reach this goal, you're going to have to learn more about the theory of probability.

Flipping coins is one of the most common ways to investigate ideas about probability. In *The Gambler's Fallacy*, you'll use coin flips to arrive at a conclusion that may surprise you. Then you'll move on to the formal definition of probability. As you'll see, people study probability through both experimentation and theoretical analysis.

Laurel Akers prepares a bar graph in order to record the results of her coin flipping experiment.

Luck and the Gambler's Fallacy

Students learn about frequency bar graphs and then explore the gambler's fallacy.

Mathematical Topics

- Frequency bar graphs
- Experimenting to determine the effect of previous coin flips on subsequent flips

Outline of the Day

In Class

1. Discuss *Homework 2: Waiting for a Double*
   - Have students share results and compute group and class averages
2. Introduce **frequency bar graphs**
   - Make a frequency bar graph of the class homework data
3. *The Gambler's Fallacy*
   - Students experiment with coin flips to see how a sequence of the same result affects the next flip
   - The activity will be discussed on Day 4

At Home

Homework 3: Expecting the Unexpected

1. Discussion of Homework 2: Waiting for a Double

As students enter and get settled, you can ask them to find the largest number of rolls needed in any of their group's experiments, to share what their individual averages were, and to find a group average for all of their experiments.

"How did you decide on your prediction?"

With the whole class, ask students how they decided on their predictions about the number of rolls it would take to get a double. They may say that you will get a double about $\frac{1}{6}$ of the time, so it will take an average of about six rolls to get a double. If they do not see this, do not press the point.

Note: Keep in mind that students' predictions in Question 1 may just be hunches. When students are asked to guess or to make a prediction, they should not have to worry that their guesses might be incorrect.

• *Examining the spread of values*

"What were the highest and lowest scores you got?"

Ask students to look at the spread of values that individuals got for the number of rolls required to get a double. In particular, you can ask what their lowest and highest values were.

For example, in a given student's ten experiments, the number of rolls required for a double might have gone from as low as 1 (first roll was a double) to as high as 15 or more (first double was on the fifteenth roll).

You might use the word "range" to refer informally to the "spread of values" just described. But as formally used in statistics, "range" means the *difference* between the highest value and the lowest value. Thus, if the largest number of rolls that was needed is 15 and the smallest is 1, then the range is 14.

For your information: It is likely that about half the students will have gotten at least one value as large as 15, and it would not be surprising if some students got values as large as 30 or more. Students do not have to understand why they are likely to get such large values.

• *Finding a class average*

Let groups share the group averages they found at the beginning of class, and let them compute an overall class average.

Careful! To get the class average, do not just average the group averages. Unless all the groups are the same size, averaging the group averages may give a different result from averaging the individual students' averages.

Ask students how various averages—the average for an individual student, the average for a group of four, or the average for a large group—vary in predictability. They will probably have an intuitive sense that the average becomes more predictable as the group gets larger. (This issue is the central focus of the Year 4 unit, *The Pollster's Dilemma*.)

For your information: A computer simulation based on 300 repetitions of the "roll to a double" experiment (30 students, ten trials each) suggests that the class average will usually be between 5.7 and 6.3. This result should reinforce any earlier suggestion that the average should be about 6. Averages for individual students will vary more widely, with most falling between 4 and 8.

2. Frequency Bar Graphs

"Have you ever made a frequency bar graph? What is it?"

Ask the class if they have ever made a **frequency bar graph.** If someone has, then you can have a volunteer explain what the term means. (It need not be a perfectly stated definition, as long as it conveys the general idea that such a graph shows how often different events occur.)

As a class, make a frequency bar graph of the number of rolls needed before getting a double. That is, each bar of the graph will show how many times a particular number of rolls was needed.

You may want to have each group compile its totals for how many 1's, how many 2's, and so forth, they got altogether, and then put the group totals together. (Be careful not to impose too much structure on this activity; let students participate in developing the ideas.)

For example, the overall class graph might look something like this.

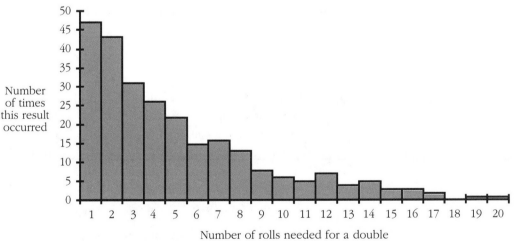

Comment: If students have agreed that 6 is the average, they may be surprised to see that there are far more results below 6 than there are above 6. For this situation, although the *mean* is 6, it can be shown that the *median* is 4 and the *mode* is 1.

Following tomorrow's discussion of tonight's homework, students will make more frequency bar graphs and will consider ways to combine bars to create a less cumbersome graph.

• *Likely versus most likely*

"What is the difference between 'most likely' and 'likely'?"

You may want to take this opportunity to talk about the distinction between *most likely* and *likely*. For example, a result of 1 is the most common single result for the doubles experiment, but it only happens about one-sixth of the time. You are much more likely to take more than one roll to get a double than to get a double on the first roll.

This may seem like a peculiar situation—the most likely result probably won't happen! But this sort of phenomenon is quite common. Another example involves flipping a coin 50 times. The *most likely* particular result is exactly 25 heads and 25 tails, but it is quite unlikely that this would happen in any given set of 50 flips. (Students will look at this experiment tonight in *Homework 3: Expecting the Unexpected*.)

3. The Gambler's Fallacy
(see page 24)

Have the class read just the introduction to *The Gambler's Fallacy*. (The title will be explained to them in tomorrow's discussion.)

"What do you think about the strategy described in the activity?"

Then, as a whole class, discuss students' reactions to the roulette strategy. There are usually three points of view.

• Students who believe that previous spins have no effect on the present spin

• Students who believe that a string of reds makes the next spin more likely to be a red, as if a trend is happening

• Students who believe that a string of reds makes the next spin more likely to be a black, as if the string must be compensated for

The Gambler's Fallacy lets students explore these three points of view in an experiment involving coin flips. In tomorrow's discussion of the activity, students will be introduced to the use of a theoretical model for such things as roulette wheels, dice, and coins, and they will see how such a model provides an explanation for the fact that the gambler's fallacy is indeed a fallacy.

Before students begin their experiments, you will need to go over the method of counting "triplets," as discussed in the directions. Be sure that students know what to do with more than three identical flips in a row. (See the "Be careful!" section of the activity.)

You may want to take a straw vote on what the students expect to happen. That is, do they expect to get more "same's," more "different's," or about the same number of each?

"What is the relationship between the roulette wheel and the coin?"

Also, you may want to ask the class what the relationship is between the roulette wheel in the introduction to the activity and the coin in the experiment. We hope someone will be able to state clearly that in both examples there are two possibilities that are equally likely. But if no student makes this observation, you need not pursue it.

Once all this introductory work is done, ask students to work in pairs on the experiment. Each pair should keep a written record of their results.

Note: If there is time only for the introductory discussion, the activity can be completed tomorrow—it is not required for tonight's homework.

- *For your information: What to expect in the experiments*

In case your students come up with surprising data and you're wondering if they did something incorrectly, here's a rough idea of what you might expect.

Each pair of students is likely to get about half a dozen triplets from their sequence of 25 flips, so in a class of about 32 students (16 pairs), you should get roughly 100 triplets. With an experiment of this size, there is about a 75% chance that the fraction of "same's" will be between 45% and 55% (inclusive) and about a 95% chance that the fraction of "same's" will be between 40% and 60% (inclusive).

If you double the number of triplets to 200 (for example, by combining results from two classes), the chance that the fraction of "same's" will be between 45% and 55% (inclusive) goes up to about 85%, and the chance that the fraction of "same's" will be between 40% and 60% (inclusive) is over 99%.

Teacher Marilyn McIntosh watches over parents Debbie and Bill Webb at an IMP Family Night.

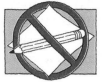

The Gambler's Fallacy

Introduction

In the game of roulette, a ball is spun around a roulette wheel, and it lands either in a red slot or in a black slot. (There is also a very small chance that it will land in a green slot, but, in this problem, we will simplify things by ignoring that fact.)

The chance of the ball landing in a red slot is the same as its chance of landing in a black slot.

Some gamblers use the following strategy for winning at roulette: They watch a wheel and if it gets a certain number of reds in a row, they bet on black, since they figure it is black's turn. Similarly, if they see a string of blacks coming up, they bet on red, since they figure red will be more likely than black after a string of blacks.

A Historical Example

In a famous incident in 1913, at the Casino in Monte Carlo, black came up a record 26 times in a row. By about the fifteenth time, people started betting overwhelmingly on red, believing that it was now "red's turn." As a result, the Casino made an enormous sum of money.

Continued on next page

The Experiment

Do this experiment with a partner.

> Flip a coin 25 times and record each flip as heads (H) or tails (T), according to the outcome.

When you have completed all 25 flips, you will have a list of 25 letters, made up of H's and T's.

Now start from the beginning of this list and find the first instance of three flips in a row that are identical (either three heads in a row or three tails in a row). We will call three identical flips in a row a **triplet**.

Record whether the flip that followed this first triplet was the *same* as the letters in the triplet or *different*. Then move to the next triplet and again record whether the flip that followed it was the same as, or different from, the letters in the triplet. Continue in this way through your whole list. (*Note:* You should ignore a triplet at the end of your 25 flips, since there is nothing following it.)

Then find out how many "same's" and how many "different's" you got.

Be careful! If you have four identical flips in a row, that gives you two triplets. For example, suppose you have H H H H T as part of your record. As shown below, the first three H's form a triplet that is followed by an H (which is the *same* as the triplet); the second, third, and fourth H's also form a triplet, and this triplet is followed by a T (which is *different* from the triplet).

This triplet is followed by H, which
is the same as the triplet.

This triplet is followed by T, which
is different from the triplet.

Similarly, if you have five identical flips, and then a different flip (such as T T T T T H), that gives three triplets: The first two triplets are followed by a flip the *same* as the letters in that triplet, while the third triplet is followed by a letter that is *different* from the letters in the triplet.

Homewook 3

Expecting the Unexpected

You know that if you flip a coin a bunch of times, you might get more heads than tails or more tails than heads, even though heads and tails are equally likely.

This activity asks you to experiment with this phenomenon and think about what is likely.

1. First gather some data by flipping a coin 50 times and recording the number of heads. Then do this 50-flip experiment again and record the result.

2. Each of your classmates will also do this 50-flip experiment twice, recording the number of heads each time.

   a. What do you think will be the largest number of heads that anyone will get in a 50-flip experiment? The smallest number of heads?

   b. About how many of the experiments do you think will give exactly 25 heads?

Interactive Mathematics Program   107

Homework 3: Expecting the Unexpected

This assignment will get students to think about the fact that events usually don't follow their theoretical probabilities exactly. Students will use the data from this assignment tomorrow to continue work on frequency bar graphs.

Emphasize to students that it will be essential for tomorrow's work that they complete this assignment. If you think it's needed, repeat the admonition against faking data.

• *Handy tips*

You might suggest to students that rather than write a sequence of H's and T's, they make a row for each category, and then just make tally marks in the appropriate row. You can also tell them about the standard technique of using a slash to mark groups of five tallies.

For instance, after 12 heads and 7 tails, their tally sheet would look like this.

You can also tell them that they can flip several coins at once, in order to save time.

What to Expect

Mathematical Topics

- Understanding that each flip of a coin is independent of the previous flips
- Distinguishing between probability based on a theoretical model and probability based on observations
- Recognizing that individual experiments rarely follow theoretical probability exactly
- Combining categories in frequency bar graphs

Outline of the Day

In Class

1. Remind students to be working on *POW 4: A Sticky Gum Problem*
2. Discuss *The Gambler's Fallacy* (from Day 3)
   - Students learn that the "gambler's fallacy" is in fact a fallacy
3. Theoretical versus observed probability
   - Introduce the idea of an **abstract model** and a **theoretical probability** for a situation

- Contrast the abstract model with **observed probability**
- Introduce the term **independent event**
4. Discuss *Homework 3: Expecting the Unexpected*
   - Make a frequency bar graph of results
   - Examine different ways to group data for a frequency bar graph

At Home

Homework 4: Coincidence or Causation?

Note: We recommend that the discussion of yesterday's activity, *The Gambler's Fallacy,* take place before the discussion of last night's homework. The material on grouping of data (which builds on last night's homework) can then, if necessary, be assigned as part of tonight's homework.

1. *POW 4: A Sticky Gum Problem—Reminder for Students*

Remind students that they should be working on *POW 4: A Sticky Gum Problem*. You may want to survey the class informally to determine the progress they are making. By now they should have solved the initial three problems, and should be able to explain clearly, for example, why the answer to Question 1 is 3 cents.

If they are stuck or confused, discuss ways in which they can help each other. You may want to provide time in class at some point for them to get into the problem.

You also may want to remind them to make up similar examples of their own and to look at how they might organize the various cases, perhaps using an In-Out table.

2. Discussion of *The Gambler's Fallacy*

Note: If students didn't have time to complete the activity yesterday, have them do that now.

Once pairs have completed their experiments and counted "same's" and "different's," have each group total their numbers of "same's" and "different's," and then compile the number of "same's" and "different's" for the class as a whole.

"Why are the number of 'same's' and the number of 'different's' so close?"

The class totals for "same's" and "different's" should be very close. You can start the discussion by asking students why this is the case. The answer should build somehow on the idea that the probability of either heads or tails is $\frac{1}{2}$.

"Does the probability of getting heads or tails change when you've had a string of flips all the same?"

To focus on the gambler's fallacy issue, you might ask if this probability changes when you've had a string of flips that are the same. Students should realize that their experiments show that the probability stays the same. (If the experiments don't show this, you'll have to improvise here, perhaps by having students generate more data.)

"Why doesn't the probability change?"

A more subtle question you might ask is *why* the probability doesn't change. If no student gives a convincing answer, you might say that a coin can't remember what the last flip was, so the probability remains the same.

• "Gambler's fallacy" defined

Tell students that the mistaken belief that a coin (or roulette wheel or die) "remembers" what has happened before, and that those past outcomes influence the future outcomes, is called the **gambler's fallacy.**

"What does the gambler's fallacy say about the roulette strategy?"

Ask students what this says about the roulette strategy described in the activity. They should be able to recognize this strategy as an example of the gambler's fallacy. If your class voiced the three points of view described on Day 3, have them discuss the analogy between those views and expectations about the coin toss experiment.

That is, students should see, for example, that believing that "a string of reds makes the next spin more likely to be a red" is like believing that the coin experiment they did would give more "same's" than "different's."

You should acknowledge that there are types of events in which past experience does change the probability of an event.

For example, the probability of a given day being rainy may be related to whether or not the previous day was rainy, since rain is a seasonal phenomenon and since a weather system often lasts several days. Even with the flipping of coins, if the person doing the flipping follows a fixed procedure, such as always flipping the coin with the same force, the result of one flip may depend on how the previous flip landed. Students will explore this issue further tonight in *Homework 4: Coincidence or Causation?*

• The gambler's fallacy and Pig strategies

"How is the gambler's fallacy related to strategies for the game of Pig?" "Did you sometimes stop rolling because you thought there was now a greater chance of rolling 1?"

You can connect the gambler's fallacy with the central unit problem by asking how the fallacy is related to strategies for the game of Pig. Specifically, you can ask if students thought the chance of rolling 1 became greater if they had already rolled something other than 1 several times.

You can sum up the discussion about the gambler's fallacy by saying that many people mistakenly believe that what has happened in the past in such a game will affect the next outcome, whereas the probability of a given outcome actually stays constant.

Comment: Students may state unequivocally that they would not be so foolish as to accept the gambler's fallacy, but in fact, most adults operate on the basis of this idea at least occasionally, even if they intellectually understand why it is false. It is not the intent of this discussion to permanently dispel this misconception from students' minds, but only to make them a bit more conscious of the trap. Sometimes just giving a name to a mistaken idea can help people identify it and make them more likely to avoid it.

3. Theoretical Models, Observed Results, and the Gambler's Fallacy

There are several important ideas that should be introduced at this point. In this section, we provide a general overview for teachers, and then give some suggestions about how to introduce the ideas to students.

• *Overview for teachers*

The statement that the gambler's fallacy is in fact a misconception and our understanding of what *should* happen in the coin-flip experiments are really based on an **abstract model.** According to this model, every flip of the coin has an equal chance of coming up heads or tails, regardless of what has happened before. The term **independent** is used to refer to events or experiments in which the result of one event does not affect the result in another.

Extensive experimental results suggest that actual coins behave similarly to this model (although perhaps the true likelihood of heads is very slightly above or below 50%, since the two sides of the coin are different). That is, for coin flips, as in many other situations, the actual results seem to be close enough to the theoretical model that one can use the model to predict complex events.

For instance, using this model, mathematical theory can predict, correctly, that the triplets experiment in *The Gambler's Fallacy* will yield about an equal number of "same's" and "different's."

The use of such models represents a high level of abstraction. Over the course of this unit, students should see that there are at least two kinds of probability being discussed— theoretical probability and observed probability.

Theoretical probability is probability determined on the basis of an abstract model. The model makes certain assumptions, such as the assumption that heads and tails are equally likely and that each flip is independent. By basing the model on such assumptions, we can then determine the probability of more complex events.

For example, by using the model for coin flips, we can determine that the probability of getting two heads when flipping a coin twice is $\frac{1}{4}$. Students will learn how to find such probabilities later in the unit by using area models and other techniques.

Observed probability is probability based on the actual results of past events. That is, we compare a current situation to previous similar situations and make a prediction based on what happened before.

For example, when a medical article says that a patient's chances of recovery are 80%, this means that of those previous cases that were like the current one, about 80% of the patients recovered.

Don't expect to be able to give crisp definitions of these two types of probability—they are not formal mathematical terms, but general categories to help us think about the ways in which we use probability.

Students should gradually build an intuitive sense of these categories and should be able to recognize the distinction when they see it. The assignments *What Are the Chances?* (Day 5) and *Homework 6: 0 to 1, or Never to Always* give them opportunities to work with these ideas.

Comment: People sometimes use the language of probability in situations that fit neither of these categories. For instance, if someone says "It will probably rain today, because I just washed my car, and it usually rains when I wash my car," that sounds like a statement using observed probability, but the speaker may never have kept track of such events. Other statements, such as "I should buy a lottery ticket today, because I'm due for a lucky break," are essentially based on the gambler's fallacy. One might call statements like these "hunch probability."

• *Introducing the ideas to students*

You can begin by pointing out to students that they have seen experimentally that the number of "same's" and "different's" came out about equal, and pointing out also that they have a reason to believe that this isn't just coincidence.

"If you flip a coin ten times and get eight heads and two tails, what's the probability of getting heads on the next flip?"

Have them imagine that they flipped a coin ten times and got eight heads and two tails, and ask what would they say at that point about the probability of getting heads on the next flip.

Here are the two main types of responses that you will probably get.

> "Perhaps it's an unbalanced coin, and the probability is about 80%."

or

> "This particular set of flips didn't fit the theory, and the probability is really still $\frac{1}{2}$."

Both are reasonable responses. Bring out, though, that there must be some "theoretical reason" for believing that the probability is $\frac{1}{2}$, in spite of the evidence, or no one would hold the second point of view.

"How would you find the probability of a thumbtack landing pointed side up?"

You can then give them the example of flipping a thumbtack, which can land with the pointed side down or with the pointed side up. Ask students how they would find the probability of the thumbtack landing pointed side up.

Since the thumbtack does not have two-sided symmetry (as the coin does), there is no theory to tell us what the two probabilities are. Students will probably suggest that they could flip a thumbtack many times and see what happens.

*"How are these
two examples—the
coin and the
thumbtack—
different in terms
of finding the
probability?"*

*"Think of examples
of each type of
probability."*

You can use this comparison, or a similar one, to identify two types of probability (as described more fully in the "Overview for teachers" above).

- **Theoretical probability,** in which a theory, or **abstract model,** explains that things should behave a certain way

- **Observed probability,** in which all you have to go on is your experience of what has happened in the past

Ask students to come up with some examples that they think represent each type of probability. Don't expect to be able to make a completely clear distinction between the two types, but try to build a recognition that there are two different perspectives.

Identify the coin-flip situation as one that involves an abstract model and the thumbtack problem as one that involves observed probability.

Introduce the phrase **independent events** to mean events or experiments in which the result of one event does not affect the result in another. For example, in the abstract model for coin-flipping, each flip is assumed to be independent. Similarly, it makes sense to assume that flips of the thumbtack are independent, so the probability is the same for each flip. (Tonight's homework explores the idea of independence in other contexts.)

- *Preview for teachers:*
  Randomness and sample size

One of the key concepts of theoretical probability is that of a **random event**. The term "random" is not formally introduced in this unit until Day 7, although the idea is used before that. (For example, the discussion introducing *POW 4: A Sticky Gum Problem* asked you to tell students that POW presenters would be chosen randomly, and *Homework 5: Paula's Pizza* says that the chef picks two toppings at random.)

Giving a general definition of the term "random" is difficult, and involves sophisticated mathematics. But in its most common usage, it refers to a situation where each possible outcome of an experiment is equally likely. For instance, a randomly flipped coin has an equal

chance of landing heads or tails; similarly, if a standard die is rolled randomly, this means that each face is equally likely to come up.

This does not mean, of course, that repeating the event many times will necessarily result in equal results for each outcome. For instance, students saw in *Homework 3: Expecting the Unexpected* that although the result of a coin toss may be randomly heads or tails, 50 tosses will usually not result in exactly 25 heads and 25 tails. (In fact, this will only happen about 11% of the time.)

Rather, "equally likely outcomes" means that as the event is repeated more and more times, the fractions representing how often each outcome has occurred will gradually get closer to each other. Thus, in general, we would expect the fraction

---

of heads in 1000 tosses of a coin to be closer to .5 than the fraction of heads in 50 tosses is. (*Note:* This idea is examined more carefully in the Year 4 unit, *The Pollster's Dilemma*.)

Students will be gaining experience in this and other probability-related units that will strengthen their intuitions about these concepts.

4. Discussion of *Homework 3: Expecting the Unexpected*

You can begin by letting students share ideas in their groups and come up with group predictions for Questions 2a and 2b.

Then ask the class for the actual outcomes, and get students' reactions—for example, ask if they are surprised or not. Be sure that they realize how rare it is to get exactly 25 heads in 50 consecutive flips. Even though it is the most likely result, it does not happen very often. (If the *most likely* versus *likely* discussion did not take place on Day 3, you should bring it up now.)

For your information: In a class of 30 students, with the 50-flip experiment done a total of 60 times, the highest result would probably be about 33 heads, and about 7 of the 60 experiments would result in exactly 25 heads.

• *A frequency bar graph of the results*

Have the class make a frequency bar graph of their data. It might look something like this.

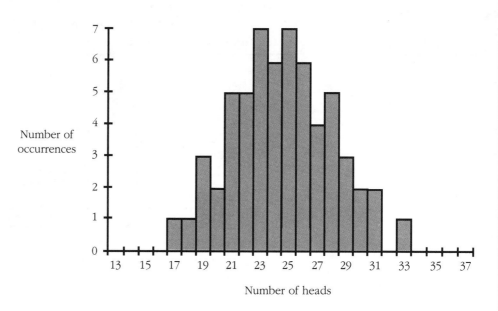

• *Grouping data*

Note: If there is not enough time for this discussion, you may want to assign a task on the grouping of data as part of tonight's homework.

"How might you group the data?"

Introduce the idea of grouping results as a way of simplifying the graph. You can let students suggest ways in which it would make sense to group the data. You may want to have each group choose its own way of grouping results and make the corresponding frequency bar graph. You can then have diamond card students present their resulting graphs.

As students present the graphs, bring out that one generally makes all groups the same "width." For example, the first graph below combines two possible results at a time, while the second combines three possible results at a time.

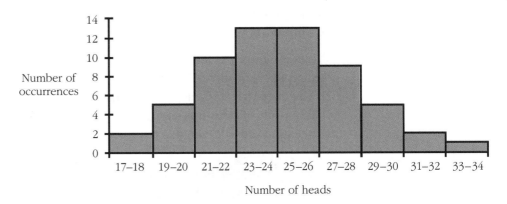

There is no formal "right" or "wrong" way to do the groupings, and students may argue about the merits of different methods. For instance, some may argue that if they are combining three bars at a time, they should work symmetrically around the value 25, so that the middle group is 24-26.

You may want to bring out the fact that, generally speaking, all of these graphs are higher in the middle and lower at the ends, whereas the frequency bar graph of the data from *Homework 2: Waiting for a Double* started out high and gradually got smaller.

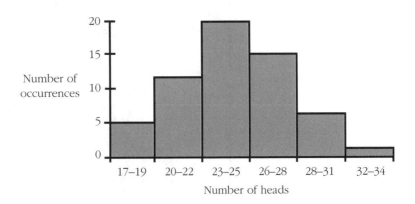

You may want to have students see what happens if they make a "mixed width" graph, and bring out that this can be misleading. An extreme example, such as combining all results 27 or over and leaving all other results as single cases, could be useful in explaining this point. With such a graph, it might appear that the most likely outcome is a result of at least 27, which would be misleading.

• **Preview for teachers**

The discussion above is intended to just briefly touch upon the idea of grouping for the sake of making frequency bar graphs. Students will do more with frequency bar graphs in later units, including work on grouping in *Is There Really a Difference?* (Year 2).

The general shape of the coin-flip graphs will be identified when students discuss the normal distribution in *The Pit and the Pendulum* (Year 1), and they will learn how to find the exact probabilities of different coin-flip results in *Pennant Fever* (Year 3). In *The Pollster's Dilemma* (Year 4), they will learn about the *central limit theorem,* which says, among other things, that as the size of the set of flips increases, the distribution of results gets closer to the normal distribution.

Homework 4: Coincidence or Causation?
(see next page)

In this homework, students are asked to decide in each situation whether previous experiences should be taken into account in determining the probability of some event. This assignment should give students further insight about the gambler's fallacy.

Homework 4

Coincidence or Causation?

Most people accept the idea that a coin doesn't "remember" its previous flips, and therefore the coin's "history" doesn't affect the probability of a given result in the future.

But there are times when previous events *do* affect future events.

In each of the following situations, you are to decide whether you think the past will or will not have a certain influence on the future.

In each case, state your decision and write a paragraph explaining why you believe that it is correct.

1. A baseball player has averaged hitting a home run once every seven games for most of the season. She has just hit a home run in each of the last three games.

   Are her chances of hitting a home run in the next game greater than, less than, or no different from usual?

2. It seems to Mr. Bryant that every time he comes along Pine Street to the traffic light at the intersection with Lincoln Avenue, the light is red. He is so infuriated with this situation that he contacts the city planner. The city planner reports that the light is set so that cars on Pine Street and cars on Lincoln Avenue are given equal time to pass through the intersection.

   If you are driving right behind Mr. Bryant one morning and come to that traffic light, do you think that your chances of getting a red light are greater than, less than, or equal to those given by the city planner?

Continued on next page

3. The Happy Days Ice Cream Cone Company claims that, on the average, only about 1 out of every 100 boxes of their famous ice cream cones will contain a broken cone. The company gladly replaces any box containing a broken cone.

You go to the store and purchase a box of Happy Days Ice Cream Cones. Upon arrival at home, you discover that one of the cones is broken. Feeling somewhat cheated, you return the box to the place of purchase and exchange it for a new box. Just to be sure, you immediately check the new box for broken cones.

Is the chance that the new box contains a broken cone different from 1 out of 100?

Equally Likely Outcomes

Students develop a formula for finding probability in situations with equally likely outcomes.

Mathematical Topics

- Understanding the difference between independent and dependent events
- Expressing probability as a number between zero and one
- Formally defining probability for equally likely outcomes

Outline of the Day

In Class

1. Discuss *Homework 4: Coincidence or Causation?*

2. Define probability more formally
   - Introduce the "0 to 1" scale for expressing probability
   - Define probability for *equally likely outcomes* as

$$\frac{\text{number of desired outcomes}}{\text{number of possible outcomes}}$$

3. *What Are the Chances?*
   - Students find probabilities for specific events using both theoretical models and observed results
   - The activity will be discussed on Day 6

At Home

Homework 5: Paula's Pizza

Special Materials Needed

- Sentence strips (for use with *What Are the Chances?*)

1. Discussion of *Homework 4: Coincidence or Causation?*

You can spend a few minutes as a class discussing each of the three situations presented. There are arguments on both sides in each case.

The goal of the discussion is to clarify the concepts involved, rather than to resolve the specific problems in the homework.

Here are some plausible arguments in each case that the new situation *does not* follow the general probabilities.

- The baseball player's chances may be greater than one in seven because she is in especially good condition, or because she is playing against a team with poor pitchers, or because she is playing in a small park for several games in a row.

- Your chances of getting a red light may be more than .5 because the lights along Pine Street are poorly coordinated with each other, or because the lights are on a timer and Mr. Bryant always leaves the house at exactly the same time.

- If the store where you bought the cones is particularly careless in its handling of merchandise, the chances of finding a broken cone may be more than one in 100. It's also possible that Happy Days exaggerates the extent of their quality control.

"Which of the homework situations involved independent events?"

Review the term *independent events*, introduced yesterday to describe events where the results of one event do not affect the results of another. Help students to see that last night's homework questions can be thought of as asking whether or not the situations described involve independent events.

2. Assigning Probabilities

The next concept to be introduced is the system of assigning numbers between 0 and 1 as probabilities.

"What are some examples of events that are impossible? Events that are certain? Events between 'impossible' and 'certain'?"

You can begin by asking students for some events that are impossible and for some events that are certain, keeping a list of students' suggestions. Then ask them for some events whose chances are between "impossible" and "certain," and list these as well.

Draw a segment of a number line with 0 and 1 on either end of it, as illustrated below.

$$0 \qquad\qquad\qquad\qquad\qquad\qquad\qquad\qquad 1$$

Tell students that mathematicians place "impossible" events at the left end of this number line, and "certain" events at the right end. Then ask students to come up and indicate where they think some "between" event from the list should be placed on the number line.

Show students the "P(…) = " notation for stating the probability of an event. For example, use the idea that, when a coin is flipped, it should come up tails half the time, and tell students that this probability is written

$$P(\text{flipping tails}) = \frac{1}{2}$$

Have students select an appropriate fraction for the probability of several of the events that are on the board. (There may not be agreement about the fractions selected. It's not important to get a consensus on this.)

• *Equally likely outcomes*

Point out that people often think of an activity as potentially having one of several different results, and tell students that the possible things that can happen in a certain situation are called **outcomes.**

"What are the possible outcomes for flipping a coin? For rolling a die? For 'handedness'?"

For example, you can ask students what the possible outcomes are for each of these activities.

- Flipping a coin (possible outcomes: heads or tails)

- Rolling a die (possible outcomes: 1, 2, 3, 4, 5, or 6)

- "Handedness" of a person (possible outcomes: left-handed, right-handed, or ambidextrous)

"How can you calculate the probability of a certain event when the outcomes are equally likely?"

Ask the class how they could calculate probability when an event has only certain outcomes that can occur, and *if* they make the further assumption that *each outcome is equally likely to happen.*

You can give as an example that one generally assumes that the two possible outcomes for the flip of a coin are equally likely, and similarly for the six possible outcomes for the roll of a die. You can bring out that these are examples of a **theoretical model.**

Students should see that the probability of any particular outcome is

$$\frac{1}{\text{the total number of outcomes}}$$

For example, if you roll a die, there are six possible outcomes, and each is equally likely. So $P(\text{rolling a five}) = \frac{1}{6}$.

Often we are interested in a particular *set of outcomes* out of some larger set. For example, out of the six possible outcomes for a die, we might want to know about the probability of rolling either 1 or 2. Elicit from the class the idea that, in general, the probability of getting a result that is within a specific set of outcomes you're interested in is expressed by the fraction

$$\frac{\text{the number of outcomes you're interested in}}{\text{the total number of possible outcomes}}$$

"What is the probability of rolling 1 or 2 with a standard die?"

"What is the probability that a person is right-handed?"

"What's the probability that someone was born in (your state)?"

You can illustrate with examples. For instance, ask what the probability is of rolling 1 or 2 with a standard die. Students should be able to explain that there are six possible outcomes; since each is equally likely, we have

$$P(\text{rolling 1 or 2}) = \tfrac{2}{6}$$

Bring out through other examples that this formula only works if the outcomes are equally likely. For example, ask students what the probability is that a person selected at random will be right-handed. Although there are three possibilities for "handedness" (including being ambidextrous), the probability that the person is right-handed is much more than $\tfrac{1}{3}$.

Another example you might use is the probability that a student in your class was born in a particular state (or country). Again, students should realize that the various possibilities are not equally likely.

Students should see that any fraction of the type

$$\frac{\text{the number of outcomes you're interested in}}{\text{the total number of possible outcomes}}$$

must be between 0 and 1, since the numerator cannot be negative and cannot be bigger than the denominator.

Bring out that if the set of "outcomes you're interested in" contains all the possible outcomes, then you are certain to get one of the results you are interested in, and the fraction is equal to 1. Similarly, an event that is impossible is said to have probability equal to 0.

Discuss the fact that probabilities can also be written as decimals or percentages. For example, students can write "P(tails) = .5" or "P(tails) = 50%" instead of P(tails) = $\tfrac{1}{2}$.

Note: Fractions, decimals, and percentages are all common ways to talk about probabilities, although the definition given above makes fractions the most natural form for the initial discussion. Students will be using all three forms during the unit.

• *For the teacher's information: The infinite case*

In the study of probability, people sometimes look at situations where there are infinitely many possible outcomes. In this context, saying that the probability of an outcome is 0 does not mean that the outcome is impossible. For example, if a whole number could be truly chosen at random, then the probability of any given result would be 0, although clearly the results would not all be impossible.

Similarly, saying that the probability of some event is 1 does not mean that the event is certain. For example, the probability is 1 that a randomly picked whole number will be at least seven, but it is possible to pick a number less than seven.

---

3. *What Are the Chances?*

(see next page)

This activity is intended to get students thinking numerically about probability, using the "0 to 1" scale for assigning probabilities, and distinguishing between *theoretical* and *observed* probability. The activity is scheduled to be discussed tomorrow.

One nice way to set up this activity is to give each group a sentence strip marked as a number line from 0 to 1 (with all the number lines the same length). Groups can then put letters on these number lines to mark the probability for each event, so that the letters will be readable when the number lines are displayed.

In tomorrow's discussion, they can display all the number lines together (for example, taped one directly below the other on the chalkboard), and the class can see how well the letters match up in position.

As you circulate among groups now, you may see that a common misconception of students is to assume that all outcomes in a situation are equally likely. Often, this misconception involves the way in which individual outcomes are identified.

For instance, in example D, students may see the situation as involving three cases—the case of two heads, the case of two tails, and the case of one of each—and so conclude that getting different results has a probability of $\frac{1}{3}$.

You may wish to clarify this by going back to example A, arguing that there are three colors, so the probability of pulling out a blue gum ball is $\frac{1}{3}$. In the context of this problem, students will probably clearly see that the colors are not equally likely to be chosen. If needed, help students to articulate that it is more useful to think of each gum ball as a possible outcome, rather than each color. Thus, they can think of the situation as having nine possible outcomes rather than three, and so the probability of getting a blue gum ball is $\frac{2}{9}$.

Then you can bring this idea back to example D. Have students work as a group to find a way to express this problem in terms of equally likely cases.

Note: On example E, students may not know that the number 1 is not a prime. You can simply tell them that, by definition, 1 is not considered to be a prime—it's not composite either, but is a special case—and move on. (You may want to explain that one can define a prime as a number with *exactly two* distinct whole-number divisors.)

When "rug games" are introduced (Day 7), students generally develop the idea of subdividing sections of the rug as needed to create sections of equal size. This is essentially the same idea as just discussed for gum balls.

What Are the Chances?

Part I: Finding Probabilities

Decide on the probability for each event below. (Some of the probabilities will be approximate.)

Describe how you decided on the probability for the events, including whether your answer was based on a theoretical model or on observed results.

A. Reaching into a bag with three red gum balls, two blue gum balls, and four black gum balls, and pulling out a blue gum ball

B. Snow falling sometime in July in Florida

Continued on next page

C. Snow falling sometime in July in New Zealand

D. Flipping a coin twice and getting different results

E. Rolling a die and getting a prime number

F. Going to a store and finding that they don't have your size in the T-shirt you like best

G. A student in your mathematics class wearing sneakers

H. Rolling two dice and getting doubles

I. Rolling a pair of dice and getting doubles by the third roll

Part II: Probabilities on the Number Line

Make a number line like the one below and put the letter of each of the events above in the proper place on the number line to indicate its probability.

0   1

Homework 5 — Paula's Pizza

Paula's favorite pizza place offers six toppings—sausage, onions, mushrooms, pepperoni, olives, and peppers.

Paula ordered a pizza with mushrooms and olives.

Unfortunately, the server only wrote down that Paula ordered two toppings, and didn't write down which two they were. The chef doesn't know Paula, and decided to pick two toppings at random.

1. How many different two-topping pizzas are possible altogether?

2. What is the probability that Paula will get the pizza that she ordered? What is the probability that she'll get something different?

3. Paula actually likes all of the toppings except sausage and pepperoni. What is the probability that she will get a pizza she likes? What is the probability that she'll get a pizza she doesn't like?

*Homework 5:
Paula's Pizza*

This assignment is a straightforward application of the definition introduced today for probability as

$$\frac{\text{the number of outcomes you're interested in}}{\text{the total number of possible outcomes}}$$

Discussing the Chances

Mathematical Topics

- Finding probabilities by counting possible outcomes
- Distinguishing between theoretical and observed probability

Outline of the Day

In Class

1. Discuss *Homework 5: Paula's Pizza*
   - Focus on making a list of cases as a method of finding probability
2. Discuss *What Are the Chances?* (from Day 5)

- Focus on examples involving theoretical probability

At Home

Homework 6: 0 to 1, or Never to Always

1. Discussion of *Homework 5: Paula's Pizza*

Note: As students get settled, you may want to remind them that yesterday's activity, *What Are the Chances?*, will be discussed after the homework, and they should be ready to present their results.

The main goal of this assignment is to reinforce the basic definition of probability as

$$\frac{\text{the number of outcomes you're interested in}}{\text{the total number of possible outcomes}}$$

You may want to begin by having a volunteer present work on Question 1. Probably the most common approach is to make a list of all the possible two-topping combinations. Such a list might be organized like this.

sausage and onions
sausage and mushrooms
sausage and pepperoni
sausage and olives
sausage and peppers

onions and mushrooms
onions and pepperoni
onions and olives
onions and peppers

mushrooms and pepperoni
mushrooms and olives
mushrooms and peppers

pepperoni and olives
pepperoni and peppers

olives and peppers

"What do you notice about the two probabilities?"

With this list of 15 possibilities, students should realize that Paula's probability of getting the pizza she ordered (in Question 2) is $\frac{1}{15}$ and that her probability of getting something different is $\frac{14}{15}$. Without making a big deal of it, bring out that the probabilities add up to 1.

Students should see that in Question 3 they just need to count that there are exactly six combinations that include neither sausage nor pepperoni. They can then conclude that Paula's probability of getting a pizza she likes is $\frac{6}{15}$ (and so the probability of getting a pizza she doesn't like is $\frac{9}{15}$).

Note: Combinatorial problems like these will be discussed extensively in the Year 3 unit *Pennant Fever*.

2. Discussion of *What Are the Chances?*

As suggested yesterday, you can have groups display their number lines together, one above the other, so everyone can see whether the letters match up from group to group.

"Are you basing your answer on observed data or on intuition?"

Be sure that students distinguish between probabilities based on theoretical models and probabilities based on observed results. For the latter, the probabilities are open to considerable interpretation. But you may want to ask students if they are basing their answers on actual observed data or just on their intuition. For example, has it ever snowed in Florida in July? Does anyone in the class actually know about the weather in New Zealand?

Although there may be more disagreement on the problems involving observed probability, you should make sure that students understand the mathematics in the examples involving theoretical probability, and get students to explain at least some of these problems.

Example A is an opportunity to get the class to articulate again the definition of probability as

$$\frac{\text{the number of outcomes you're interested in}}{\text{the total number of possible outcomes)}}$$

Students may not see why example D has a probability of $\frac{1}{2}$. If they are confused, perhaps the best approach is to list the possible outcomes. The key is realizing that getting a tail and then a head is different from getting a head and then a tail. In other words, the *equally likely* outcomes are HH, HT, TH, and TT.

Since the two flips are different in two of the four cases, the probability of getting different results is $\frac{2}{4}$. (A similar problem occurs in Question 3 of *Homework 7: Portraits of Probabilities*. A different type of explanation is used there.)

On example H, at least a few students should be able to see from a theoretical model that the probability is $\frac{1}{6}$. One approach is to imagine rolling one die first and see that the second die has a $\frac{1}{6}$ chance of matching the first; another approach is to list all 36 two-die combinations and see that six of them are doubles. You may want to point out that the answer for example H seems to match the result on *Homework 2: Waiting for a Double,* in which students saw that it takes an average of about six rolls to get a double.

On example I, students may use their experimental data from *Homework 2: Waiting for a Double,* to estimate the probability. (The theoretical value is $\frac{91}{216}$, which is about 42%, but do not expect students to be able to figure this out.)

Mariela Miranda, Erica Chavez, and Roxanne Farler work collaboratively on their chart.

Homework 6

0 to 1, or Never to Always

For each of the probabilities below, think up two situations that have the given probability.

In one of those two situations, the probability should be based on a theoretical model. In the other situation, the probability should be based on observed results. (You can be imaginative about this.)

1. Probability = 0

2. Probability = $\frac{2}{7}$

3. Probability = 75%

4. Probability = 1

5. Probability = 2.3

6. Probability = .01

Homework 6: 0 to 1, or Never to Always

Tonight's homework continues the focus on the distinction between probability based on a theoretical model and probability based on observed results. Students should realize when they do the assignment that Question 5 presents an impossible situation.

Days 7-11

Pictures of Probability

You've seen that probabilities can be expressed with fractions, percentages, or decimals, so you can see that numbers play an essential role in talking about probability.

Pictures are another important tool used to understand mathematics. In this portion of the unit, you will blend geometry with probability, using area diagrams to think about the probabilities of different events. Your next POW, *POW 5: What's on Back?*, will also involve probability, and you may find that working with area diagrams helps solve the problem.

Jessica Ehlers is using area models to determine probabilities.

114

Rug Games

Mathematical Topics

* Examples of theoretical and observed probability
* Using area models to understand probability situations

Students are introduced to the rug metaphor as an area model for probability.

Outline of the Day

In Class

1. Select presenters for tomorrow's discussion of *POW 4: A Sticky Gum Problem*
2. Discuss *Homework 6: 0 to 1, or Never to Always*
3. *Rug Games*
   • Students are introduced to the rug metaphor as an area model for probability

4. Discuss *Rug Games*
   • Have students describe how they found each probability

At Home

Homework 7: *Portraits of Probability*

1. POW Presentation Preparation

Presentations of *POW 4: A Sticky Gum Problem* are scheduled for tomorrow. Choose three students to make POW presentations, and give them overhead pens and transparencies to take home to use in their preparations.

2. Discussion of *Homework 6: 0 to 1, or Never to Always*

As students get settled, you may want to ask them to share their two situations for Question 2 or 3 with their group members.

You can ask the heart card students from different groups to state the events they thought of for various probabilities, and have them explain why they saw their examples as observed or theoretical. Allow opportunity for discussion of both the categorization of each example and the probabilities involved. (For the "observed" examples, it may be hard to come to agreement about the probabilities.)

"Why is it impossible to have an event whose probability is 2.3?"

Be sure to have a student explain why it's impossible to have an event whose probability is 2.3.

Note: Some students might need a discussion of the relationship between fractions, decimals, and percents in these problems. If so, look for opportunities to do this casually in the course of a discussion about probability.

3. *Rug Games*
(see page 58)

Today's activity introduces an area model for thinking about probability. The rug metaphor will be used for most of this unit and will gradually be replaced by the standard term *area model*.

Introduce the activity to students with this tale.

> I have a rug at my house, and there is a trap door in the ceiling directly over the rug. The trap door has the same shape and size as the rug. From time to time the trap door opens and a dart drops directly down onto the rug. The process is quite **random**, which means that any point of the rug has as good a chance of getting hit as any other.

> Now, of course, my guests never sit directly on the rug itself (it's dangerous!), but they like to sit around the outside of the rug and guess which part of the rug will get hit by the next random dart. To keep things interesting, I have a variety of rugs of the same size that I can put out on different occasions.

"Which color would you predict?"

Have students look at the first rug in the activity *Rug Games*, and ask them which color they would predict. (You can show students a transparency of the rug on the overhead projector. A page for making this transparency and a page for the other rugs in the activity are in Appendix B.)

Students will probably see that there is more gray space than white (they may or may not express this in terms of area) and conclude that they would predict that the dart would land on gray.

"What is the probability for gray? For white?"

Then ask them to find the probability for each color. (They may need to trace the diagram in order to do this.)

Have several groups share their reasoning. You may want to have them come up and show any additional lines they used to find the probabilities. The final diagram might look like this.

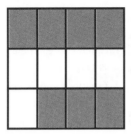

Ask students to write the probabilities for each color using the "P(…) = …" notation introduced on Day 5. Thus, they should get P(white) = $\frac{5}{12}$ and P(gray) = $\frac{7}{12}$.

After this introduction, have students work on the rest of the activity in their groups, deciding which color they would predict and finding the probability that the dart will land on each color. (In some examples, groups may be able to figure out which color has the greatest probability of being hit by a dart before they actually find each probability.)

If students want to add additional lines to the diagrams to analyze the areas, you can suggest that they trace the diagrams on other paper. If groups finish the activity, you can ask them to create a new rug for another group.

4. Discussion of Rug Games

Have students share their answers to the rug problems. Students will probably break each rug up into equal-sized pieces. Be sure to relate this process of subdivision to the idea of equally likely events.

For instance, rug A can be divided as shown below into 15 same-sized pieces, each of which has an equal chance of being struck by a dart. Since 8 of the 15 pieces are gray, P(gray) = $\frac{8}{15}$. Similarly, P(white) = $\frac{7}{15}$.

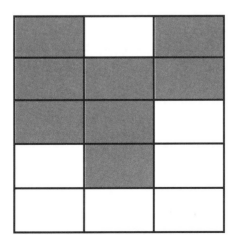

Rug Games

Imagine that each diagram in this activity represents a rug. A trap door opens directly over the rug and a dart falls down, landing at random somewhere on the rug.

"At random" means that every point on the rug has as good a chance of getting hit as every other point.

1. If you were trying to predict which part of this rug will get hit, which color would you choose, gray or white? What is the probability of being hit for each color?

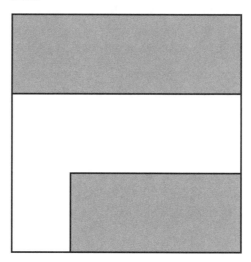

Continued on next page

Tell students that they will be using the rug model to find the answer to various probability problems and that eventually this model will help them to evaluate strategies for the game of Pig.

2. For each of the rugs below, decide which color you would predict as most likely to be hit. For each color, find the probability of being hit.

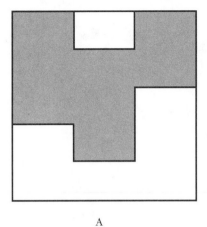

A

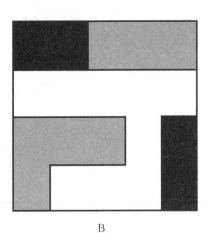

B

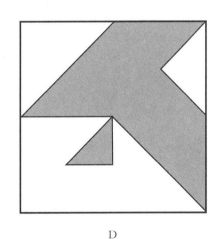

C

D

You can informally introduce the language of area into the discussion. For example, you can say that the gray portion of rug A represents a larger area than the white portion.

Note: Students should have some intuitive ideas about area. The concept of area is discussed more fully in the Year 2 unit *Do Bees Build It Best?*

Homework 7 Portraits of Probabilities

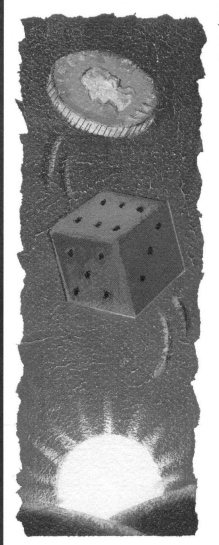

Part I: Rugs for Events

Do these three tasks for each of the events numbered 1 through 5 below.

- State the probability of the event happening.

- Write a short explanation of why you believe you are correct.

- Draw a rug with a shaded portion that represents this probability.

1. Rolling a 6 with one die.

2. Being chosen as one of three POW presenters out of a class of 30 students.

3. Flipping a coin twice and getting two heads.

4. The sun rising tomorrow.

5. Having no homework for the rest of the semester.

Continued on next page

Homework 7: Portraits of Probabilities

In this homework, students will create rugs to describe events and will create events that go with given rugs.

Part II: Events for Rugs

For each of the rugs illustrated, describe an event that you believe has the probability of occurrence represented by the shaded part of the rug.

6.

7.

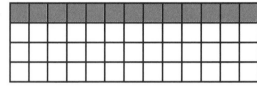

8.

9.

Interactive Mathematics Program

Interactive Mathematics Program

POW 4 Presentations

Students continue to work on "rugs," present POW 4, and are introduced to POW 5.

Mathematical Topics

- Working with area models for probability
- Developing general formulas for problem situations

Outline of the Day

In Class

1. Discuss *Homework 7: Portraits of Probability*

   - Focus on rug diagrams for finding probability
   - Use 2 × 2 diagram for finding probabilities for outcome of two coin flips

2. Presentations of *POW 4: A Sticky Gum Problem*

   - Focus on the use of variables and generalization

3. Introduce *POW 5: What's on Back?*

   - Discuss what an "experiment" might be for this problem
   - Discuss the importance of doing experiments many times

At Home

Homework 8: *Mystery Rugs*

POW 5: *What's on Back?* (due Day 13)

Discuss With Your Colleagues

Getting Productive POW Discussions

There is a risk that students and teachers, wanting to be supportive, will be reluctant to criticize student presentations.

What do you do when students present incorrect mathematics? You don't want to embarrass anyone, yet you cannot leave students with the wrong information. How can you handle this?

More broadly, how can you make POW discussions more productive? How can you encourage students to challenge each other in a constructive way?

A related issue involves how much comprehension you should expect from a class on a given POW. When is it worthwhile to push the class further in their understanding of an idea? What is the right point to stop work on *POW 4: A Sticky Gum Problem?*

1. Discussion of *Homework 7: Portraits of Probability*

• *Part I: Rugs for Events*

You can give transparencies and pens to groups 1 through 5 and have each group prepare a visual aid for the discussion of the problem that corresponds to their group number (group 1 presents Question 1, group 2 presents Question 2, and so on). Each group may elect to synthesize its members' answers or use one particular member's answer. You can ask the spade card student to make the presentation for the group (even if a different student's answer is used).

"What are other ways to draw a rug for this situation?"

As presentations are made, ask the rest of the class for alternative ways to draw a rug for a given problem.

For instance, Question 1 asks them to draw a rug with a shaded portion that represents a probability of $\frac{1}{6}$. Students will probably create a rug that has six equal sections, with one shaded. But this can be done in various ways, as shown in the diagrams below.

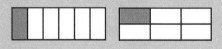

Also, the rug need not show six equal parts, but could just show two

sections, one representing $\frac{1}{6}$ and the other representing the remaining $\frac{5}{6}$, as illustrated below.

Students will probably explain Questions 2 and 3 in terms of a theoretical model. (Questions 4 and 5 are for amusement and to show the extreme cases of 0 or 1 probability.)

Question 3 is similar to example D of *What Are the Chances?* (Day 5), in which students were asked to find the probability of flipping a coin twice and getting *different* results. Some students may still see the flipping of a coin twice as having three equally likely possible outcomes—two heads, one head and one tail, and two tails. It is important that students realize that these outcomes are *not* equally likely.

In the discussion of *What Are the Chances?*, we suggested using a list of cases as a means of explaining the two-coin situation. Now that students have experience with area diagrams, you should help them to see how this two-coin situation can be explained using area diagrams. Experience with a two-dimensional diagram like the one below will also be useful when students analyze the two-dice sum problem (*The Theory of Two-Dice Sums,* Day 10).

If no student suggests it, introduce a rug diagram like the one shown here.

This diagram should help convince students that the three outcomes—two heads, one head and one tail, and two tails—are not equally likely. They will probably agree that it is more useful to think of two coin flips as having four possible outcomes, so that one can work with outcomes that are equally likely. Using two different coins (for example, a penny and a dime) can be useful in helping students see each box as representing a distinct outcome.

If students are still skeptical, you can take a few minutes to conduct an experiment. Have each student flip a pair of coins (labeled somehow as "coin #1" and "coin #2") a few times and compile the results for each portion of the diagram. About 100 cases should be enough to show that the four outcomes seem equally likely, or at least to show that the combination of the two "one of each" cases is more likely than either "two heads" or "two tails."

Suggestion: You may want to post this diagram as well as urge students to save it for later reference. They will be asked to explain this situation again in *Homework 10: Coins, Coins, Coins;* as noted above, this type of diagram will be useful in the Day 10 activity, *The Theory of Two-Dice Sums.*

• *Part II: Events for Rugs*

Let students share some of the situations they created for Part II of the homework. Of course, you should expect a wide variety of responses here.

2. Presentations of POW 4: A Sticky Gum Problem

Have the three selected students present their solutions to the POW.

"Does anyone have a generalization that hasn't been mentioned?"

If none of the students making presentations generalized the problem, then ask the class if anyone else did so and have those people also make presentations.

> There are various levels of generalizations of this problem. At this early stage in the curriculum, it is possible that no one arrived at a general formula, but this is a good problem to use to show students what is meant by a generalization.
>
> The problem also provides a good constructive opportunity to look at what distinguishes a POW from an ordinary homework assignment—the focus on generalization and exploration.

If no one has made any generalizations, you can begin with the case of the twins, and n colors. You can have students make an In-Out table like the one below, which includes their answers to Questions 1 and 2.

Number of colors available	Number of gum balls needed
2	3
3	4
4	?
5	?

"How many gum balls are needed with four colors? With five colors? With n colors? Can you explain the generalization?"

They should be able to figure out various individual cases here, and to generalize that n colors could require as many as $n + 1$ gum balls. They should also be able to explain their generalization with a statement like, "The worst case would be if she got one of each color first; but, if that happened, then the next one would have to repeat a color she already had."

"What happens with the triplets?"

You could go from there to the case of the triplets, using a similar table and getting $2n + 1$ as the most that Mr. Hodges might need in order to get three of one color for his triplets.

As a possible hint:
"What's the most
that Mr. Hodges
could spend
without satisfying
his triplets?"

One helpful way to look at the triplet case is to ask what is the most that Mr. Hodges could spend *without* satisfying his triplets. Students should be able to see that the worst-case scenario is getting exactly two of each color. Once this has happened (with $2n$ gum balls), the next gum ball will give him three of one color.

The important issue here is not the specific formulas involved, but the process of trying different examples, organizing the information, looking for patterns, expressing them symbolically, and explaining the patterns.

3. Introduction of POW 5: What's on Back?
(see next page)

Take some time in class to introduce this POW, since it involves complex ideas involving strategy as well as the need to distinguish between experimental and theoretical probability.

It is important that students understand that in this POW a strategy consists of deciding what to do in response to what is shown on the drawn card. Also, emphasize that they are just not looking for the *best* strategy, but are to analyze *several* strategies. (See discussion on Day 13 for more details.)

"In this POW, what does it mean to 'experiment'?"

One part of the POW is designed so that students get an experimental estimate of certain probabilities. Help students to see that in the POW, to "experiment" means to set up a situation using cards like those described and actually carrying out the strategy a number of times. Each time they pick a card, they make a prediction based on that strategy. They record how often the prediction turns out to be correct.

"How many experiments might you need to do?"

You will probably need to stress that doing just a few experiments is not very meaningful. You might remind them of their earlier experience with coin tosses (for example, in *Homework 3: Expecting the Unexpected*). They saw that even 50 flips didn't guarantee an accurate reflection of the theoretical probabilities.

> *Note:* Students won't fully analyze the significance of sample size until Year 4, in *The Pollster's Dilemma*, but they should begin to appreciate it intuitively.

Since students have no theoretical basis on which to judge how many experiments are needed, you will probably need to discuss how they should handle this. The POW itself suggests that they watch to see when their overall probability for a given strategy stabilizes. That is, when the experimental estimate stops changing substantially every few trials, then students can be reasonably confident that they are close to the actual value.

You may also want to ask students to discuss the difference between experimental results and results derived from a theoretical model. You can point out that although an experiment gives them a feel for what the results

POW 5

What's on Back?

In a certain game, there are three cards.

- One card has an **X** on both sides.

- One card has an **O** on both sides.

- One card has an **X** on one side and an **O** on the other side.

The three cards are placed in a bag, and the bag is shaken. You draw out one card and look at one side only. You cannot look at the other side or at the other cards. The goal is to predict whether there is an **X** or an **O** on the other side of the card you drew out.

There are many strategies for doing this, some good, some not as good. Here are two possible strategies.

- Predict that the mark on the other side will be different from the mark you see. (That is, if you see **X**, predict **O**; and if you see **O**, predict **X**.)

- Always predict that the mark will be an **X**.

No strategy will be successful all of the time, so you should try to find the probability of success for each strategy you consider.

Your ultimate goal is to find the strategy that has the highest possible probability of being right.

Continued on next page

might be, it does not guarantee an accurate picture of the probability, even with a large number of trials. But if the theoretical analysis gives a result very different from the experimental estimate, then one might suspect an error in the theoretical analysis.

Remind students that they are to work on the POW a little bit each night and not save it for the last moment.

For each strategy you consider, do these two tasks.

    a. Find an *experimental estimate* of the probability of success using that strategy. That is, devise an experimental method of testing your strategy. It will probably be useful to make a set of cards to do this.

       You will need to repeat your experiment quite a few times in order to get a good experimental estimate. You may want to keep repeating it until your overall results begin to stay roughly the same as you repeat the experiment.

    b. Analyze the probability of success for that strategy by using a *theoretical model*.

Begin with the two specific strategies described above, looking for both an experimental estimate and a theoretical analysis for the probability of predicting correctly with each of those strategies.

Then look at other strategies, trying to determine the strategy with the highest probability of success for correctly predicting "what's on back."

Write-up

Your write-up should contain these four parts.

1. *Problem Statement*

2. *Process:* Include a description of exactly what you did to carry out the experiments for part a.

3. *Results:* Describe each strategy you tried. For each strategy, tell what you found as the probability of predicting correctly. If you can, describe your results in terms of both

    a. your *experimental results*

    b. your *theoretical analysis*

    Also state what strategy you think gives the highest probability of predicting successfully, and justify this answer.

4. *Evaluation*

Homework 8

Mystery Rugs

In each of the following situations, you are given some information about the probabilities of certain outcomes.

Your task in each problem is to

- make up a situation with outcomes that fit the given probabilities

- draw and label a rug that shows the probabilities of each outcome

1. There are two possible outcomes for an experiment. One of the outcomes has a probability of $\frac{2}{7}$.

2. There are three possible outcomes for an experiment. One outcome has a probability of .4, and a second outcome has a probability of .25.

SEASONS OF THE YEAR

3. There are three possible outcomes for an experiment. One outcome has a probability of 50%, the second outcome has a probability of 30%, and the third outcome has a probability of 25%.

Homework 8:
Mystery Rugs

The homework above incorporates a review of fractions into further work with rugs. Note that Question 3 presents an impossible situation (unless the outcomes overlap), because the probabilities add up to more than 1. Do not tell students this—they should figure it out on their own.

DAY 9
The Counters Game

The counters game introduces students to two-dice sums.

Mathematical Topics

- Creating situations that have a given set of probabilities
- Developing strategies for a game

Outline of the Day

In Class

1. Discuss *Homework 8: Mystery Rugs*
2. *The Counters Game*
   - Students play a game involving strategy and probabilities for the sum of two dice
3. Discuss *The Counters Game*
   - Use the game to spark interest in two-dice sums

At Home

Homework 9: Rollin', Rollin', Rollin'

Special Materials Needed

- A pair of dice for each group of students
- 11 counters and a strip of paper for each student

1. Discussion of Homework 8: Mystery Rugs

Let some students share the situations they created for Questions 1 and 2, and ask the class to evaluate whether the situations fit the information. Be sure that students find the missing probabilities ($\frac{5}{7}$ and .35, respectively).

We hope that students will have seen that Question 3 presents an impossible situation because the total of the probabilities is more than 1. If not, you can try to build on their work in finding the missing probability in Questions 1 and 2 to uncover the difficulty.

If students come up with a solution to Question 3 by creating overlapping events, that's fine, and they should be commended for their creativity!

2. *The Counters Game*

(see facing page)

A major purpose of this activity is to motivate tomorrow's activity, *The Theory of Two-Dice Sums*. Each individual will need a strip of paper and 11 counters, and each group will need a pair of dice.

Begin by having students read the instructions for the game. A demonstration will answer most of their questions about how the game is played.

Then have each student make a game board and let the groups work through steps 1 through 3 of the activity.

Note: The number of dice rolls needed to complete a game will depend both on luck and on how the individuals place their markers. A calculator simulation suggests that you will rarely get a winner in fewer than 20 rolls, but with "reasonable" placement, you will usually get a winner within 60 rolls.

• *Group competition*

After students have played a few games and have written and thought about strategies, bring the class together and let them know that they are about to have a group versus group competition, as indicated in Question 4 of the activity.

Tell them that each group will use a single game board and will need to come up with a collective decision about where to place its counters. If necessary, give groups a few minutes to formulate and write down their strategies.

When all the groups have placed their counters, begin rolling the dice. Continue until one group has removed all of its counters. You can then move on to the discussion.

3. Discussion of *The Counters Game*

"Explain the strategy that your group used."

Ask groups of students to explain their strategy in placing counters. Use the phrase **two-dice sum** to refer to the sum of the numbers on the two dice. Here are some questions to consider.

• Did some two-dice sums come up more often than others? Why?

• Is it best to put all of your counters on the two-dice sum that you think will come up the most often?

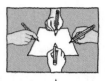

(for Questions 2 and 4 of the activity)

The Counters Game

The Game

Each player in this game needs a board, which consists of 11 boxes numbered from 2 through 12, as shown below.

2	3	4	5	6	7	8	9	10	11	12

At the start of the game, players each place 11 counters on their individual boards. The counters can be placed in the different boxes in any way the player chooses (including putting more than one counter in a single box).

During the game, a pair of dice is rolled repeatedly, and the numbers on the dice are added each time. Every player who has any counters in the square corresponding to the sum of the dice removes *one counter* from that square. (Even if a player has more than one counter in that square, only one counter is removed. If a player has no counters in that square, the player does nothing on that roll.)

The winner of the game is the first player whose counters are all removed.

The challenge of the game is to initially place the counters so that they will be removed as quickly as possible during the game.

The Activity

1. Play one or two practice games in your group. Just guess about where to place the counters.

2. Now, think about where to place the counters. Write a sentence or two explaining what you think would be a good way to place them and why.

3. Play some games in your group, with each member of the group using her or his own strategy for placing the counters.

4. Discuss the different strategies used in your group, in preparation for a competition between all the groups. Choose a single strategy to use in the competition, and state what this strategy is.

"How can you find the theoretical probability of each two-dice sum?"

A major goal of the activity is to get students interested in the following question (which you should raise if no else does).

> *How can you find the theoretical probability of each two-dice sum?*

Answering this question is the task of Days 10 and 11. You can let students speculate about this question, but you should not try to resolve it today.

Note: The mathematical analysis of strategies for the counters game is quite complex and is not part of this unit. But we expect that students will see, through their experience in this game, that some two-dice sums (such as 6, 7, and 8) come up more frequently and other two-dice sums (especially 2, 3, 11, and 12) come up very rarely. Their intuition should suggest that it makes sense to concentrate their counters in the boxes whose numbers come up more often.

For your information: Here are some facts about certain strategies.

Strategy 1: Place one counter in each box.

A calculator simulation indicates that with this strategy it takes an average of about 60 rolls to remove all the counters. (It will usually take fewer rolls, but will occasionally take many more, which brings up the average.)

Strategy 2: Place one counter on 4, one counter on 5, two counters on 6, three counters on 7, two counters on 8, one counter on 9, and one counter on 10.

A calculator simulation indicates that with this strategy it takes an average of about 30 rolls to remove all the counters.

Strategy 3: Place all the counters on 7.

A theoretical analysis shows that with this strategy it takes an average of 66 rolls to remove all the counters.

The second strategy described is not necessarily the best possible, but it clearly seems to be better than the first or the third.

Homework 9: *Rollin', Rollin', Rollin'*

The purpose of this homework is to help students see a pattern in the results of rolled dice and to help them get some ideas on how to organize that information into graphical form.

Homework 9   Rollin', Rollin', Rollin'

Roll a pair of dice 50 times and record the sums in an organized way.

1. Draw a graph of the data you gathered.

2. Write a paragraph about your results. You should summarize your observations about the data and discuss why the results come out the way they do.

3. What new thoughts does this experiment give you about how to play the counters game?

A Model for Two-Dice Sums

Students develop an area model for finding the probability of each two-dice sum.

Mathematical Topics

- Using an area model to analyze two-dice sums

Outline of the Day

In Class

1. Form new random groups
2. Remind students to be working on *POW 5: What's on Back?*
   - Discuss how they are doing their experiments
3. Discuss *Homework 9: Rollin', Rollin', Rollin'*
   - Make a frequency bar graph of class data
   - Calculate and post the percentages for each two-dice sum (for comparison with theoretical analysis on Day 11)
4. *The Theory of Two-Dice Sums*
   - Students use an area model to find the theoretical probability of each possible two-dice sum
   - The activity will be discussed on Day 11

At Home

Homework 10: Coins, Coins, Coins

Special Materials Needed

- A red die and a white die (or other colors) for each group of students
- A blank bar graph, such as that shown in the discussion of *Homework 9: Rollin', Rollin', Rollin'* (you may want to use a piece of large graph paper, a transparency, or the blackboard for this)

1. Forming New Groups

This is an excellent time to place the students in new random groups. Follow the procedure described in the IMP *Teaching Handbook*, and record the groups and the suit for each student.

2. *POW 5: What's on Back?*— Reminder for Students

"How far have you gotten on your POW?"

If students haven't yet done their experiments: "How could you carry out your experiment? How many experiments might you need?"

"Do you think you might use a 'rug' for a theoretical model?"

Remind students to be working on *POW 5: What's on Back*. By now they should have begun work on finding the probability of success, at least experimentally, for the two strategies given.

If they have not done so, you can ask why. You may need to take class time to talk about how to carry out the experiments, perhaps focusing on the first of the strategies described in the POW. Let students brainstorm, either in groups or as a whole class, to come up with ideas on how they could make and use a sample set of cards like those in the POW to test the strategy.

You may also want to review the idea that students need to do more than a handful of experiments to get a good experimental estimate of the probability of success.

You should also remind students that they are to look for a *theoretical* analysis of the probability as well as an experimental estimate. You can suggest that they look at a "rug model" of the situation.

3. Discussion of Homework 9: *Rollin', Rollin', Rollin'*

You might begin the homework discussion by asking students how they kept a record of their results. For example, some may have written down the results in the order they occurred, while others may have listed the possible outcomes and then made a tally mark next to a number each time they got that outcome. If no one mentions the second method, you might suggest it yourself, since it provides an easy way to keep track of how often each outcome occurred.

Then have some students share the graphs they drew and any general conclusions they reached. Presumably students found that the data showed only a few very high sums (10, 11, or 12) or very low sums (2, 3, or 4), with most of the sums in the middle (5 through 9). More detailed results will come as they compile their data.

Have each group compile the data from the students in their group, and then ask the club card member of each group to report the number of 2's, 3's, . . . , 12's from their group, while you list these amounts on the board. Have students find the total number of occurrences for each possible two-dice sum.

Then have them compile these totals into a frequency bar graph, with a bar for each possible sum, perhaps using grid butcher paper or a transparency of grid paper. Before making the graph, they will need to choose an appropriate scale for the vertical axis. (You can expect about 250 7's in a class of 30 students.)

The completed version might look something like the diagram below. (It's helpful to write in the column totals on the graph, so you don't have to read them off the scale.)

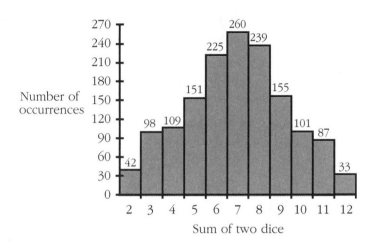

"What should the sum of the column totals be?"

You can also ask students what they think the sum of the column totals ought to be. (It *should be* 50 times the number of students in class.) Find the actual column totals, and tell students to use this information to find the percentage of occurrences for each sum.

Save these results for comparison with the theoretical analysis to be done in today's activity, *The Theory of Two-Dice Sums* (see the heading "Comparing Theory and Experiment on Two-Dice Sums" in tomorrow's discussion).

"How does this graph compare to your individual graphs?"

Once the graph is compiled, discuss how it resembles the graphs of their individual homework assignments and how it differs. You should encourage comments about the class graph being "more even," "smoother," "more symmetrical," and so forth, than their individual graphs.

Note: Students may have been uncertain about what sort of graph to draw for homework. If students portrayed the information in other ways, that's okay, and these other ways can be shared with the class.

4. *The Theory of Two-Dice Sums*
(see facing page)

Tell the students that they are now going to look at a rug model as a way of finding the *theoretical probability* for each of the possible two-dice sums.

Give each group a red die and a white die (or other colors). Using dice of two different colors will help students understand that, for example, there are two ways to roll a 3 and a 5, while there is only one way to roll two 4's.

Let students begin work on *The Theory of Two-Dice Sums*. You will need to decide whether they are making progress on their own or if it would be more productive to bring them together to share ideas and get some hints from you. (You may want to look at the Day 11 discussion about this activity and tonight's homework for ideas of what to expect from students.)

The Theory of Two-Dice Sums will be discussed tomorrow. If you see a group today that has a clear understanding of the activity, you might ask them to prepare a presentation for tomorrow.

If students seem stuck, one option is to have them turn their attention to the homework, which is closely related to the activity. They may get some ideas about two-dice sums from the homework, and they may be able to complete their work on *The Theory of Two-Dice Sums* as part of their homework.

> *Note:* Students should be made aware that the term "rug diagram" is not standard, and that "area model" is the more common term. The transition to using the term "area model" can be gradual—the term *rug* will continue to be used in student materials for much of the unit.

• •

The Counters Game

Students really enjoyed playing this game, endeavoring to be the first group to clean off their game board.

   "Let's do it again!", "Roll a 2!"

   "No, roll a 5! We need a 5!"

IMP Year 1 Teacher

The Theory of Two-Dice Sums

You have played a game that involved two-dice sums, and you have done some experiments to get an idea of how two-dice sums are distributed.

Now it's time to look at the theory and to get more precise information about this distribution.

Work with your group to develop a rug diagram that will help you understand two-dice sums and provide a theoretical model for finding the probability of each possible sum.

Keep in mind that equal areas of your rug should represent equally likely events. You should assume that the dice are fair. That is, for a single die, the probability of getting each possible result is $\frac{1}{6}$.

You may find it useful to use two dice, preferably of different colors, as you work. Think about the portion of your rug that corresponds to a given result on the dice.

124

Homework 10 Coins, Coins, Coins

1. Binky was working on Question 3 from *Homework 7: Portraits of Probabilities*, which asks for the probability of getting two heads if you flip a coin twice.

   She said that if you flip twice, there are exactly three possible outcomes— two heads, one head and one tail, and two tails—and so the probability of getting two heads is $\frac{1}{3}$.

   Explain why she's wrong. Make your explanation as clear as you can, using diagrams as needed.

2. Imagine that you have two pockets and that each pocket contains a penny, a nickel, and a dime.

   You reach in and remove one coin from each pocket. Assume that, for each pocket, the penny, the nickel, and the dime are equally likely to be removed.

   a. What are the possible amounts you could get for the total of the two coins?

   b. What is the probability that your two coins will total exactly two cents?

   c. What is the probability for each of the other outcomes in Question 2a?

3. What do Questions 1 and 2 have in common, and how are they related to the problem of two-dice sums?

Homework 10: Coins, Coins, Coins

You should alert students that this assignment refers to problems done earlier in the unit, so that they can be sure to take home any notes that relate to those earlier problems.

DAY 11

A Model for Two-Dice Sums, Continued

Students complete their analysis of the two-dice sum problem.

Mathematical Topics

- Using an area model to analyze two-dice sums

Outline of the Day

In Class

1. Discuss *Homework 10: Coins, Coins, Coins*
   - (Discussion might be omitted if students made good progress on *The Theory of Two-Dice Sums*)
2. Discuss *The Theory of Two-Dice Sums* (from Day 10)
   - Use a 6 × 6 diagram to show equally likely outcomes

Find the probability for each two-dice sum

3. Compare the theoretical analysis to the experimental results from *Homework 9: Rollin', Rollin', Rollin'*

At Home

Homework 11: Two-Dice Sums and Products

Discuss With Your Colleagues

How Much Mastery for Two-Dice Sums?

Students are spending two days developing the probabilities for two-dice sums, and then using them in some further problems. But this doesn't mean that it is important that they know these probabilities.

What is important is that they understand the idea of an area model, and that they are able to rediscover these probabilities if they are needed.

How do you balance "understanding the concept" with "knowing the facts"?

1. Discussion of *Homework 10: Coins, Coins, Coins*

You may decide to omit a direct discussion of this homework assignment, since its main purpose is to suggest an approach to *The Theory of Two-Dice Sums*.

If your students seem to have made good progress yesterday, you can go directly to the discussion of their ideas on two-dice sums. But if they seem to need hints, you can go over some or all of the homework as a way of getting them to think about the two-dimensional diagrams that are used in today's discussion of *The Theory of Two-Dice Sums*.

You can begin with Question 1, which is a review, and get students to focus on the two-dimensional nature of the diagram. They should see that because the problem involves two coins, it makes sense to set up the diagram with the result of one coin along the top and the result of one coin along the side. They should use the diagram to show that the three outcomes Binky describes are not equally likely.

Similarly, for Question 2 of *Homework 10: Coins, Coins, Coins*, you can move them toward a diagram like the one below.

	Left pocket		
	penny	nickel	dime
Right pocket penny	2¢	6¢	11¢
nickel	6¢	10¢	15¢
dime	11¢	15¢	20¢

Students should see that each of the nine boxes is equally likely, and they should then be able to find the probabilities.

Rather than explicitly discuss Question 3, you may just want to suggest that students incorporate the methods used in the homework into their analysis, looking for ways to get equally likely outcomes.

2. Discussion of *The Theory of Two-Dice Sums*

If students seemed stuck yesterday or didn't finish, you can give them more time to work on this activity, and you can build on the homework discussion. Otherwise, you can go directly to presentations of their work.

By drawing an analogy to their work on the homework problems, students should end up with a diagram labeled something like this.

White die

	1	2	3	4	5	6
1	2	3	4	5	6	7
2	3	4	5	6	7	8
3	4	5	6	7	8	9
4	5	6	7	8	9	10
5	6	7	8	9	10	11
6	7	8	9	10	11	12

Red die

"Which squares are most likely when rolling two dice?"

To emphasize the "equally likely" aspect of the problem, you can ask which square (row and column) would be most likely if you were rolling two dice. Students should articulate that each square is equally likely, with a probability of $\frac{1}{36}$.

"What's the probability of getting a red 3 and a white 6?"

You can also ask for the probability of getting various individual combinations, such as 3 on the red die and 6 on the white die. Students should see that each such combination has a probability of $\frac{1}{36}$.

"What part of the diagram represents a roll of 4 on the white die?"

You might also want to ask them, for example, to identify the portion of the diagram that represents a roll of 4 on the white die.

By the end of the discussion, students should realize that there are 36 equally likely outcomes for the pair of dice, and they should be able to find the probability of each of the 11 possible sums (2 through 12). They will probably find these probabilities by counting squares for each sum and dividing by 36. For example, the probability of getting 6 as the two-dice sum is $\frac{5}{36}$, since five of the 36 boxes have a sum of 6 in them.

There is no reason to have students memorize the table of probabilities for the different sums, but they should know how to find those probabilities by using a diagram like the one above.

• *Optional: Further questions on two-dice sums*

Here are some additional questions you can pose to the class to strengthen and clarify their understanding of the rug model.

• Why are there two ways of getting a sum of 3, when the only way to get it is with a 1 and a 2? (The use of differently colored dice should help students understand this

situation. They should see that "red = 1, white = 2" is a different square on the rug from "red = 2, white = 1.")

• What is P(even number)?

• What is P(multiple of 5)?

You can have students create and answer more questions like these if it seems needed in order for them to understand the ideas.

3. Comparing Theory and Experiment on Two-Dice Sums

"What would the totals have been if the experiments had followed the theoretical probabilities perfectly?"

Have students compute what their class totals would have been on *Homework 9: Rollin', Rollin', Rollin'* if the experiments had followed the theoretical probabilities perfectly. Describe the answers as the **theoretical distribution** (or *theoretical probability distribution*).

You can have students make a graph of this theoretical distribution and compare it to the graph of their experimental data. They will probably see some general similarity, but they will also see that their results varied somewhat from the theoretical distribution.

"Which was closer to the theoretical distribution—your individual data or the combined class data?"

You might ask them to consider which was closer to the theoretical distribution—students' individual data or the combined class data, and why.

Homework 11

Two-Dice Sums and Products

Suppose you roll a pair of dice and add the numbers that you roll.

1. Which is more likely—that the sum is an odd number or that the sum is an even number? Explain why.

2. Make up two new probability questions about two-dice sums that can be answered from the rug diagram for two-dice sums. Answer your two questions if you can, and explain your answers.

Now suppose that instead of adding the numbers on the two dice, you *multiply* them. Let's call the result a **two-dice product**.

3. What are the possible two-dice products? What is the probability of getting each of the two-dice products?

4. Which is more likely—that the two-dice product is an odd number or that the two-dice product is an even number?

5. Make up two probability questions about two-dice products, and answer them if you can.

Homework 11:
Two-Dice Sums
and Products

This homework gives students experience in finding simple probabilities, and it also has them make up their own questions about probabilities.

Days 12-21

In the Long Run

In recent activities, you have looked at ways to find the probability of a given event, such as flipping two heads in a row or getting a sum of 9 on a pair of dice. For example, you've flipped coins or rolled dice to determine the probability of a particular outcome. You've used "rug diagrams" to analyze probabilities and have confirmed some of your results with experimental evidence.

In the game of Pig, the probabilities are pretty simple, because each number on the die is equally likely to occur. But the situation is complicated by the fact that the payoff differs with each possible result and ranges from a gain of six points to a loss of all points.

This page in the student book introduces Days 12 through 21.

Kristin Livingston, Katy Anderson, Emily White, and Megan Hall discuss strategies for "The Counters Game."

How do you use probability to analyze what will happen in the long run in a game like this? This unit looks first at simple situations involving the long run, then gradually works toward more complex problems. You're moving toward your goal of finding the best strategy for Pig!

DAY 12 *Spinners*

Mathematical Topics

- Using a spinner as a probability model
- Using the "large number of trials" approach to find the average in the long run

Students use a spinner game to study what happens "in the long run."

Outline of the Day

In Class

1. Select presenters for tomorrow's discussion of *POW 5: What's on Back?*
2. Discuss *Homework 11: Two-Dice Sums and Products*
3. *Spinner Give and Take*
   - Students use a spinner game to explore what happens "in the long run"
4. Discuss *Spinner Give and Take*
   - Bring out the idea that one player wins more often but the other player wins more money each time
   - Have students share results

- Use the "large number of trials" approach to find out what happens in the long run
- Students see that small variations in the number of times each outcome occurs won't change which player wins overall
- Students see that the average gain or loss per turn is the same no matter how many turns are used in the analysis

At Home

Homework 12: Pointed Rugs

Special Materials Needed

- A paper clip for each pair of students

1. POW Presentation Preparation

Presentations of *POW 5: What's on Back?* are scheduled for tomorrow. Choose three students to make POW presentations, and give them pens and overhead transparencies to take home to use in their preparations.

You may want to suggest that the presenters each focus on a different aspect of the problem. For example, one might talk about results with the first strategy, another with the second, and a third might talk about finding the best strategy. However, it's probably wise to leave the decision to them, since they may not all be comfortable with the whole problem.

2. Discussion of Homework 11: Two-Dice Sums and Products

You can let students share with their groups the questions they made up for Questions 2 and 5, while volunteers prepare presentations on Questions 1, 3, and 4.

Students probably will have answered Question 1 by adding up the appropriate probabilities. For example, to find the probability of an even sum, we add P(2) + P(4) + P(6) + P(8) + P(10) + P(12). So the probability of an even sum is

$$\frac{1}{36} + \frac{3}{36} + \frac{5}{36} + \frac{5}{36} + \frac{3}{36} + \frac{1}{36} = \frac{18}{36} = \frac{1}{2}$$

One way to recognize that odd and even sums are equally likely, without actually adding up the probabilities, is to notice that in each row of the rug diagram there are three even sums and three odd sums.

On Question 3, students will have to go through the same kind of analysis that they did for *The Theory of Two-Dice Sums*. (It turns out that there are more possibilities for two-dice products than there are for two-dice sums. The most common products are 6 and 12, each with a probability of $\frac{1}{9}$.)

On Question 4, students should see that even products are more common. You may want to ask for an explanation for why this problem has a different answer from Question 1. Someone may be able to articulate that a product is odd only when both factors are odd, which happens one-fourth of the time.

3. Spinner Give and Take
(see facing page)

Spinner Give and Take is the first of several activities in which students must consider not only the probabilities for various outcomes, but also certain "values" associated with the different outcomes.

This activity also introduces the "large number of trials" approach to figuring out what happens in the long run. This approach will be used throughout the rest of the unit, as well as in later units involving probability.

You can demonstrate the method for making a spinner (see diagram on *Spinner Give and Take*).

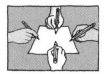

or

Spinner Give and Take

Al and Betty are playing a game with the spinner shown at the left.

Each time the spinner comes up in the white area, Betty wins one dollar from Al.

Each time the spinner comes up in the colored area, Al wins four dollars from Betty.

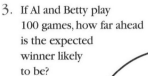

Al wins $4 from Betty

Betty wins $1 from Al

1. In the long run, which of the two players is more likely to be the winner in this game? Write down your prediction and explain your reasoning.

2. Now play the game for 25 spins and write down what happens.

3. If Al and Betty play 100 games, how far ahead is the expected winner likely to be?

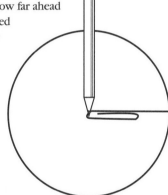

Suggestion: You can make a spinner using a pencil and a paper clip, as shown at the right, by bending open one end of the paper clip and then using the pencil to hold the other end in place as the paper clip spins.

Bend open a paper clip so that a point sticks out. It is the paper clip that will do the spinning. Place a pencil through the loop of the paper clip, pointing down, into the center of the circle on the worksheet. Hold the tip of the pencil firmly on the center of the circle with one hand and flick the paper clip so it spins around.

We recommend that you have students work in pairs on *Spinner Give and Take*. You can begin the discussion of the activity when you see that all the groups have finished Questions 1 and 2, since Question 3 is primarily for the follow-up discussion.

4. Discussion of *Spinner Give and Take*

• Question 1

"How did you make your predictions for Question 1?"

To begin the discussion, you can have several pairs of students explain their predictions from Question 1 and give their reasoning. Roughly speaking, they should realize that although Betty wins more often, Al wins more money each time he wins.

They will have to do quantitative work to support their predictions. They may do this in terms of a specific number of spins (for example, 100), estimating how many times each would win and then figuring out how much each would win. Or they may do it in a more abstract way (for example, "She wins three times as often, but he wins four times as much when he wins").

Many students may be uncomfortable with the more abstract approach, so you should try to get at least one explanation that involves a specific number of spins.

• Question 2

"What result did you get for Question 2?"

Ask several pairs of students to give their results from Question 2. Probably some pairs will have ended up with Betty ahead, although most should have Al ahead.

"Does the fact that some pairs showed Betty winning mean that the reasoning was wrong?"

Ask students if having Betty win for some pairs means that their reasoning in Question 1 was wrong. (If the class wasn't clear about what they expected to happen, you can ask a similar question, such as "What does that tell you about the predictions?")

"What does 'the long run' mean in Question 1?"

If necessary, call the students' attention to the phrase "in the long run" in Question 1. They should gradually be developing and articulating the idea that although any result might occur in a small number of spins, in the long run the number of times each person wins is roughly proportional to the probabilities.

You may want to pool the results from all the groups to see how many times Al and Betty each won altogether. Students should see Al winning about $\frac{1}{4}$ of the time and Betty winning about $\frac{3}{4}$ of the time (unless there is something causing the spinners to be unbalanced).

You may want to come back to these numbers after the discussion of Question 3 and find out how much each won altogether.

• *Question 3*

If students didn't yet get to Question 3, you can now give them time to work on it.

Follow the students' lead in the discussion of the problem, but guide them toward an analysis that goes something like this.

"What's Betty's probability of winning? Al's?"

1. From the shading of the spinner, Betty's probability of winning a given spin is $\frac{3}{4}$ and Al's is $\frac{1}{4}$.

"How many times out of 100 should Betty win? What about Al? How much do they each win?"

2. If Betty and Al spin 100 times altogether, and the results follow the probabilities, then we can expect Betty to win about 75 times and Al to win about 25 times. Betty would win $1 from Al in each of her 75 victories, and Al would win $4 from Betty in each of his 25 victories.

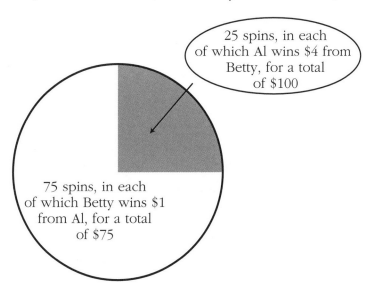

25 spins, in each of which Al wins $4 from Betty, for a total of $100

75 spins, in each of which Betty wins $1 from Al, for a total of $75

"How far ahead is Al altogether?"

3. So in 100 spins, Betty will win about $75 from Al (75 · $1) and Al will win about $100 from Betty (25 · $4). Thus, over the course of 100 spins, Al would be about $25 ahead of where he started.

• *Al wins even with some variation in the results*

"How many spins would Al have to win in order to come out ahead?"

Emphasize the fact that, in any particular set of 100 spins, a variety of results are possible. You might ask students how many spins Al would have to win (out of the 100) in order to come out ahead. They will see that he has some leeway, but not much. Specifically, he needs to win at least 21 of the 100 spins to come out ahead of Betty. (If he wins 20 spins, and she wins the other 80, they break even.)

> The fact that Al wins even if the results are slightly off from the probabilities is part of the strength of the "large number of spins" approach.
>
> Students should develop an intuitive sense that the more spins are played, the more likely it is that Al will come out ahead.

• *Varying the number of spins*

"Try it with a different total number of spins."

Have students do the same analysis with at least two different numbers of spins. They should see in each case that Al comes out ahead, but they should also see that he wins more money if they play more spins. For example, if the same analysis is done for 200 spins, Al comes out $50 ahead.

You can then ask what is the same in each case, besides the fact that Al is ahead. If necessary, point to the fact that, for example, if they do twice as many spins, this analysis shows him winning twice as much.

"How much did Al win per spin, on the average?"

As a final hint, ask how much he won, on the average, per spin. Students should see that in each case, the average is 25¢. Put another way, his end result is the same as if he had won 25¢ on each spin.

> On Day 14, the unit will introduce the term **expected value** as a shorthand for this idea of "average per spin." For now, the goal is that students begin to agree that "average per spin"
>
> is a good way to measure what happens in the long run, since the outcome is the same no matter how many spins are made.

• *Spinners and Pig*

"How does this problem relate to the game of Pig?"

Ask students how they think this problem relates to the game of Pig. You may want to use this question as a topic for focused free-writing, and then have students share their ideas.

As needed, remind students that in the game of Pig, too, they are interested in what happens in the long run. Specifically, they want to know which strategy is likely to produce the most points per turn in the long run.

You can mention that finding the probability of a given result for a particular strategy in the game of Pig is much harder than finding the probabilities for this simple spinner game.

Homework 12   Pointed Rugs

In *Rug Games,* you decided which color was most likely to be hit by a falling dart for each of the rugs below. In this homework you are asked to work again with these rugs. But in this assignment, points are awarded for each color. This means that your choice of color involves more than just finding probabilities—you must also take into account the number of points that are awarded each time that the dart lands on a certain color.

For each rug, decide which color is the best to bet on to maximize your points in the long run. (*Hint:* Imagine dropping a dart a large number of times, and decide which color would be likely to give the most points.)

Write clear explanations to support your answers.

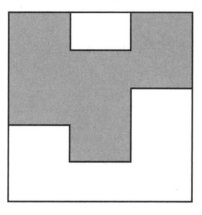

A		B	
Gray	6 points	Gray	10 points
White	8 points	White	8 points
		Black	16 points

Continued on next page

Homework 12: Pointed Rugs

You may wish to emphasize to students that these are the same rugs that were used in the *Rug Games* activity on Day 7. They can use the probabilities that they found for that activity.

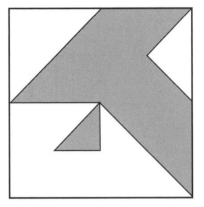

C

Gray	5 points
White	6 points
Black	10 points

D

Gray	15 points
White	13 points

POW 5 Presentations

Students consider "pointed" rugs and also present POW 5.

Mathematical Topics

- Working with weighted probabilities
- Estimating probabilities by using experiments
- Analyzing strategies by using an area model

Outline of the Day

In Class

1. Discuss *Homework 12: Pointed Rugs*
   - Students see that small variations in the number of times each outcome occurs won't change which color wins overall
2. Presentations of *POW 5: What's on Back?*

- Focus on theoretical analysis for specific strategies

At Home

Homework 13: Mia's Cards

POW 6: Linear Nim (due Day 18)

Special Materials Needed

- Transparencies of rug diagrams from the activity *Rug Games* (see Day 7)

1. Discussion of Homework 12: Pointed Rugs

You can assign one or two groups to each problem of the homework and have them prepare a presentation of their solution for the class.

While groups are preparing presentations, you may wish to make note of who did the homework and see how well they seem to have understood the ideas in the assignment. Finding the probability for each color is a repetition of their work on *Rug Games* (Day 7). The new element in the assignment is taking the points into account.

If students had difficulty with the problems, you can suggest to groups that they pick a convenient number of games to play and see which color would have the greatest total number of points if the darts landed according to probability. As noted earlier, this "large number of trials" method is used throughout the unit, so be sure that it is presented.

When groups are ready to make their presentations, you can have the diamond card member of each group present the group's work.

"Did all of you use the same number of games?"

You can ask if other students used the same number of games. Since this number will probably have varied, you can bring out that the predicted winning color is the same no matter how many games are played (although the total number of points for each color will change with the number of games).

"What should you consider in choosing the number of games to represent 'the long run'?"

You can suggest that students pick a convenient number when they decide upon the "large number of times" they imagine dropping a dart on the rugs. For example, in rug A, the probabilities for the colors are $\frac{8}{15}$ and $\frac{7}{15}$ for gray and white respectively, so it makes sense to use a multiple of 15 for the sample number of times they drop a dart.

• *Small variations don't affect who the winner is*

As with yesterday's discussion of *Spinner Give and Take,* you may want to point out that although the results usually won't follow the probabilities exactly, the fraction of darts landing in each color should be close to the probabilities in the long run. Bring out that if the total number of darts is large, slight variations from the theoretical probabilities won't change which color yields the most points.

2. Presentations of POW 5: What's on Back?

• *For teachers: What should students get from this POW?*

This may be a difficult POW for many students, and it is a good opportunity for you to think about the purpose of having students do problems like these.

Keep in mind that the mathematical content of most POWs is not material that students must master in order to move successfully through the curriculum. Although the content of *POW 5: What's on Back?* is related to that of the unit, students certainly don't need to know the best strategy for this prediction problem in order to be successful in the unit.

For many students, this unit will be their first significant exposure to concepts of probability, so you should measure your success and theirs in terms of their *growth* of understanding, rather than by some arbitrary absolute standard.

Even if students come away from this problem without a complete understanding of it, they probably will have strengthened their appreciation of several ideas, including these three:

- How to carry out an experiment to estimate a probability

- Learning that the accuracy of an experimental estimate will generally depend on how many times the experiment is done

- The use of an area diagram as a tool for finding the theoretical probability of an event

• *The presentations*

Have the three students give their POW presentations.

The discussion should focus primarily on students' work on the two specific strategies outlined in the activity.

"What were other people's experimental results?"

Bring out in the discussion of the experimental results that an experiment will give a more accurate estimate if it is repeated more often. You may want to have other members of the class report their experimental estimates.

As presenters discuss their theoretical analyses, you might need to point out that they should be using a model in which each of the six sides (for the three cards) is equally likely to be the initial side viewed. (This is equivalent to considering each card to be equally likely, and then having each side of the chosen card be equally likely.)

• *Possible strategies*

In determining the best strategy, you may first want to identify what the possible strategies are. Focus students' attention on strategies that are based on what shows up on the side of the card that is drawn out of the bag.

In other words, each strategy that students consider should look something like this:

If you get a card with **X** showing, then predict ___.

If you get a card with **O** showing, then predict ___.

(Although the strategies described in the POW aren't set up like this, they could be phrased in these terms.)

Note: There are also various "gambler's fallacy" strategies, such as "Predict the opposite of what the last card showed." You can talk about these as well if students are interested.

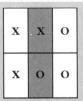

- *Background for teachers: A sample theoretical analysis*

The following description is an example of how the theoretical analysis of a strategy might proceed. You can use the ideas contained in this description as background to help you give hints or suggestions to students.

Begin with a rug diagram for the problem. In the illustration below, sections above or below each other represent the two sides of a given card.

Suppose you want to analyze the strategy of always predicting the mark different from the one you see (which is the first strategy mentioned in the POW).

If the first box (which has an **X**) is the one seen, then a player using this strategy would predict **O**, and would be incorrect, since the reverse side is an **X**.

But if the second box in the first row (which also has an **X**) is the one seen, then a player using this strategy would again predict **O**, and this time would be correct, since the reverse side is an **O**.

A similar analysis applies in other cases. The two boxes shown shaded in the next diagram represent the cases where the prediction would be correct, and the unshaded boxes represent the cases where the prediction would be incorrect.

In other words, for this strategy, we have P(success) = $\frac{1}{3}$.

A similar sort of analysis could be done for the strategy of always predicting **X**. This strategy would predict correctly if the side initially picked corresponds to one of the boxes shaded below. This gives P(success) = $\frac{1}{2}$ for this strategy, making it better than the previous one.

It turns out that neither of the strategies above is the best one. The best strategy is to always predict the same mark as the one you see. This strategy would predict correctly if the initial side chosen corresponds to one of the shaded boxes below. So P(success) = $\frac{2}{3}$ for this strategy.

One way to prove that this strategy is the best is to analyze them all. There are only four strategies available of the type described earlier in this discussion. The fourth one—always predicting **O**—has a probability of success of $\frac{1}{2}$, just like the strategy of always predicting **X**.

Homework 13

Mia's Cards

1. Mia is playing a game that involves picking a card from a standard deck. A standard deck consists of 52 cards, with 13 cards in each of 4 suits. The suits are clubs, diamonds, hearts, and spades. The 13 cards in each suit are called the ace, 2, 3, 4, 5, 6, 7, 8, 9, 10, jack, queen, and king.

   In Mia's game, she mixes up the cards and then picks a card at random from the deck. She gets 10 points if it's a heart and 5 points if it's a club, spade, or diamond. Then she puts the card back in the deck.

   If she does this many times, what will be her average number of points for each time she picks a card? Explain your answer.

2. On February 14, Mia changes the game so that she gets 20 points for a heart, 15 points for a diamond, and no points for a club or a spade. If she plays this new game many times, what would you expect her average score per card to be?

3. a. Make up a game like Mia's, in which a person picks a card and receives a number of points that depends on the type of card picked.

   b. Calculate the average score per card in the long run for your game.

Homework 13:
   Mia's Cards

Mia's Cards is similar to the spinner and rug games discussed in earlier activities except that finding the probabilities is more difficult because the situations are more complex.

Students may find this to be a difficult assignment. After the concept of expected value is introduced tomorrow, you can use the students' games (Question 3) as examples on which they can apply the concept, if needed.

POW 6: Linear Nim
(see facing page)

This POW continues the theme of strategy and also can involve the kind of two-variable analysis that students may have used in *POW 4: The Sticky Gum Problem*. Since the POW involves a game played with two players, you may want to suggest that students work on it in pairs.

You may want to take a couple of minutes to have two students play a game or two in front of the class to be sure everyone sees how the game works.

This POW is scheduled to be discussed on Day 18.

Erica Dommer and Shannon Campbell discuss their area model for "One-and-One" (Day 15).

POW 6   *Linear Nim*

There are many strategy games in which two players take turns removing objects from one of several piles according to certain rules, with the winner being the person who removes the last object.

These games often go by the name Nim.

In one version of the game there is only one pile. In that case, you can represent the objects by a single row of marks on a piece of paper, and so we will call this game Linear Nim.

Here's how a particular form of Linear Nim works.

> At the beginning, there are 10 marks on a piece of paper, as shown below.
>
> | | | | | | | | | |
>
> Each player, in turn, crosses off 1, 2, or 3 of the marks.
>
> Play continues until all of the marks have been crossed out. The player crossing off the last mark is the winner.

Part I: Finding a Strategy

Your first task in this POW is to find a winning strategy for this particular game.

You might want to begin by finding a partner and playing the game together for a while.

Continued on next page

As you and your partner play, pay attention not only to who wins, but also to when you realize who is going to win and how you know.

The question of who wins may depend on which player goes first. So one element of your strategy might be deciding whether you want to go first or second.

Be sure that the strategy you develop is complete. That is, you should take into account every possible move that your opponent might make.

Part II: Variations

Once you have developed your strategy for this particular game, investigate how the strategy would have to change if the game were to vary in different ways.

The particular game above starts with 10 marks and allows a player to cross out up to 3 marks at a time. What if these numbers were changed? For instance, suppose you start with 15 marks instead of 10, or allow a player to cross out up to 4 marks at a time instead of 3? In other words, you can change the *initial number* of marks and you can also change the *maximum per turn* that a player can cross out.

How would your strategy change if you varied the game? Are there some cases where you should choose to go first and others where you should choose to go second? What does it depend on?

Consider a variety of examples and look for generalizations.

Write-up

1. *Process:* Describe how you went about understanding the original game and developing a strategy. Indicate the key insights you had that were important in your understanding.

2. *Strategies*

   a. Describe the strategy you developed for the original game.

   b. Describe some specific variations you looked at and what the strategy was for each.

3. *Generalizations:* State any general principles you developed about variations on Linear Nim. In particular, can you describe, in terms of the *initial number* and the *maximum per turn,* how to decide whether to go first or second?

4. *Evaluation*

Expected Value Defined

Expected value is formally defined, and students use the concept in several situations, including the unit problem.

Mathematical Topics

• Expected value

Outline of the Day

In Class

1. Discuss *Homework 13: Mia's Cards*
   • Delay discussion of Question 3 until after expected value is defined
2. Introduce the term **expected value**
   • Emphasize that "expected value" is just a new name for an idea students have already encountered

• Restate the results of previous problems in terms of expected value
3. Restate the central problem in terms of expected value

At Home

Homework 14: A Fair Rug Game?

1. Discussion of *Homework 13: Mia's Cards*

You can have students share their homework with one another in their groups, and as they are doing so, you can give some groups overhead transparencies. Assign one or two groups each to Questions 1 and 2, and have the other groups choose a game that one of their members made up for Question 3.

• Questions 1 and 2

The presentations should help students feel comfortable in working with a large number of games, finding the total number of points, and then finding the average by dividing by the number of games.

> In Question 1, if students use 100 games, Mia will get about 25 hearts, for 250 points, and about 75 cards from the other suits, for 375 points, giving her about 625 points for 100 games, or an average of about 6.25 points for each card picked.

Work through at least one example where the average is computed by using two different total numbers of games. For instance, you might have students do Question 1 using 200 games, in which case Mia will get a total of about 1250 points. Students should recognize that her average is still about 6.25 points for each card, and they should begin to see intuitively that this average will be the same no matter what the total number of games. *Note:* This issue is explored further in the supplemental problem *Expected Conjectures*.

Keep the results of Questions 1 and 2 handy so you can state them again in a moment, using the language of expected value.

• Question 3

You can postpone discussion of the games that students made up until after the term *expected value* is introduced.

2. Expected Value

Introduce the term **expected value** for "average amount gained (or lost) per turn in the long run," and ask students to restate their results from *Homework 13: Mia's Cards* using this phrase.

For instance, for the game in Question 1, they can say that for each card picked, Mia has an expected value of 6.25 points.

> *Note:* For emphasis, it's a good idea to use a phrase like *per game* or *per turn* whenever you use the term *expected value.* For example, in the paragraph above, it was stated that Mia had an expected value of 6.25 points "for each card picked."

"So we expect Mia to get 6.25 points each time, right?"

You can play devil's advocate by making a statement like, "So each time Mia picks a card, we expect her to get 6.25 points." Students should respond by clarifying that the expected value is an average in the long run, and not what one expects in any given turn.

Emphasize that *the concept of expected value is nothing new!* We have just given a short name to one's average gain or loss per turn in the long run. You can point out that the use of such terminology makes it easier to state complex ideas.

> • **Warning: Avoid the "probability method"**
>
> You may be familiar with an approach to expected value in which the probability of each possible outcome is multiplied by the point value for that outcome, and the results are added to give the expected value. Although this approach—the "probability method"—is mathematically equivalent to the "large number of trials" approach, it lacks the concrete and intuitive feel that the large number of trials gives, and most students seem to find the probability method less clear.
>
> Therefore, we have avoided that method, and recommend that it not be introduced at this time. If individual students create it on their own, however, there is no reason why they can't use it. But after acknowledging their work, move on without turning it into a lesson for the whole class.
>
> *Note:* The probability method for finding expected value is discussed in the Year 4 unit *The Pollster's Dilemma.*

• *Looking at other examples*

"Can you describe the question from 'Homework 2: Waiting for a Double' in terms of expected value?"

Have students look back at *Homework 2: Waiting for a Double*, in which they found the average number of rolls needed for a pair of dice to get a double. Ask them to try to express what they did in that activity in terms of expected value. Help them to see that the work they did there gave an experimental estimate of the expected value for the number of rolls needed.

If students are having difficulty finding expected value, use some of the games they made up for Question 3 of last night's homework in order to solidify the idea. Even if they do seem comfortable with the concept of expected value, you might just take a few minutes to let groups share some of their variations and let students work on these for fun.

3. Connecting Expected Value to the Game of Pig

"How can you use the term 'expected value' to restate the unit problem?"

Ask the class how the concept of expected value can be used to restate their goal in analyzing the game of Pig.

Connecting expected value to Pig is important for this unit, since expected value is one of the unit's primary concepts. It is important in terms of motivation for students to realize that they are looking for the Pig strategy that yields the highest expected value per turn.

Tell students that later in the unit they will find the expected value for various strategies for a game much like Pig, and they will find the strategy for Pig that gives the highest possible expected value.

Homework 14   A Fair Rug Game?

1. Tony and Crystal are sitting around a rug watching darts randomly fall from the ceiling.

   The rug they are using is pictured above.

   If the dart lands on the white part of the rug, Crystal wins $5 from Tony. If it lands on the black part, Tony wins $3 from Crystal.

   Do you think this is a fair game? What is Tony's expected value for each turn? What's Crystal's?

2. If you think the game is not fair to one of the players, change the amount of money they each win in order to make the game fair. (Don't change the rug.)

Homework 14:
A Fair Rug Game?

This problem introduces the notion of a **fair game** and also requires students to use negative numbers for expected value.

A One-and-One Situation

A one-and-one situation illustrates the difference between "most likely result" and "expected value."

Mathematical Topics

- The concept of a **fair game**
- Using a simulation to approximate a probability problem

Outline of the Day

In Class

1. Discuss *Homework 14: A Fair Rug Game?*

2. *One-and-One*
   - Students speculate about the most likely outcome of a one-and-one situation
   - No further discussion is needed

3. Simulation of a one-and-one situation

At Home

Homework 15: A Sixty-Percent Solution

Special Materials Needed

- Paper bags
- A large collection of red and yellow cubes (other materials will work as well, as long as the two types of objects are not distinguishable by touch)

1. Discussion of *Homework 14: A Fair Rug Game?*

Ask for a volunteer to present Question 1 to the class, but leave for later the question of whether the game is fair.

The first step in the problem is to recognize that $\frac{9}{15}$ of the rug is black and $\frac{6}{15}$ is white. (There is no particular need for students to simplify these fractions.) So one observation that could be made is that Tony wins more often than Crystal. But students should recognize that who wins how often is not the only factor here, since the payoffs are different.

Probably the presenter will describe a "large number of trials" analysis. For example, if there are 150 games, Tony will win about 90 times and Crystal will win about 60 times. This means that Tony will win about 90 • 3 = $270 from Crystal while losing about 60 • 5 = $300 to her, for a net loss for Tony of about $30.

This is the first example involving a net loss, so students may need some guidance on how to express Tony's expected value. The idea of using a negative number will probably occur to many of them, and you only need confirm that this is, indeed, the standard way to express the idea that, over the long run, Tony loses money. Thus, Tony's expected value per game is –$.20 (or –20¢).

When you move on to Crystal's expected value per game, you can bring out that her gain must exactly match Tony's loss, since their game is a "closed system." This can be confirmed by going through the analysis separately for her.

• Is it fair?

"What does 'fair' mean in this context?"

With the separate expected values determined, return to the initial question of whether the game is fair or not. You may need to ask students to come up with a definition of "fair" in this context. They will probably agree that a **fair game** is one in which the players should come out even in the long run.

So this game is not fair, because Crystal comes out better in the long run than Tony.

• Question 2

"How can you change the game to make it fair?"

With the definition of fairness clarified, let volunteers offer their suggestions about how to change the game to make it fair. The smallest whole number solution is to have Tony win $2 from Crystal when the dart lands on black, and to have Crystal win $3 from Tony when the dart lands on white, but any payoff in the same 2 : 3 ratio will work.

2. *One-and-One*
(see page 112)

One-and-One and the related follow-up activities have two main purposes.

- To clarify the distinction between "expected value" and "most likely outcome"

- To have students find expected value in more complex situations than those they have encountered previously

For your information: A "one-and-one" occurs in a special type of penalty situation, that is, after one player has committed a foul against another. The player who has been fouled is allowed to take a free throw.

If the free throw is *not* successful (that is, if it doesn't go into the basket), then the one-and-one situation is over. But if it *is* successful, then the player gets to shoot once again (but only once more). Each successful shot scores one point.

Thus, the player can end up with 0 points (by missing the first shot), 1 point (by making the first shot, but then missing the second), or 2 points (by making both the first and the second shots). Make sure everyone understands the situation, acting it out if that seems at all necessary.

Ask whether any of the students can explain what a "one-and-one" situation is in basketball. If not, you will need to do so.

Once the one-and-one situation has been explained, have students look at the specific situation described in *One-and-One,* in which Terry has a 60% chance of success on each of her attempted free throws. You can clarify this by asking how many shots she would be likely to make out of 100; out of 40; out of 15; and so on.

"In a one-and-one situation, how many points is Terry most likely to score: 0, 1, or 2?"

Then have students move on to the question posed in the activity:

> In a one-and-one situation, how many points is Terry *most likely* to score: 0, 1, or 2?

Let them think briefly about this individually, without discussion. Get the class to vote on the three possible answers, and record the results of the vote. (No further discussion is needed here.)

Then move on to the simulation described after the activity.

During an IMP teacher inservice, Steve Hansen demonstrates to Sylvia Turner another way to approach the problem.

One-and-One

Sometimes in a basketball game, a player is presented with a situation known as a "one-and-one."

In a one-and-one situation, the player begins by taking a free throw. If the player misses, that's the end of it. But if the shot is successful, the player gets to take a second shot.

One point is scored for each successful shot. So the player can end up with 0 points (by missing the first shot), 1 point (by making the first shot, but then missing the second), or 2 points (by making both the first and the second shots).

Terry is a basketball player who has shown over a period of time that whenever she attempts a free throw, she has about a 60% probability of making it.

> In a one-and-one situation, how many points is Terry *most likely* to score: 0, 1, or 2?

Write down your intuitive guess about the answer to this question.

Adapted from *The Middle Grade Mathematics Project Series: Probability,* by Lappan et al., © 1986 Addison-Wesley Publishing Co., Inc.

3. One-and-One Simulation

• *The general idea of a simulation*

Tell students that they are going to use an experiment to estimate the probabilities involved in the question posed in *One-and-One*.

Point out that they don't have Terry available to them, so they can't test the actual situation. Tell them that what they will do instead is carry out an experiment that is mathematically equivalent.

"Where have you heard the term 'simulation' before?"

Introduce the word **simulation.** You can ask students where they have heard the term before (for example, flight simulators) and why people use simulations. The main idea to get across is that a simulation allows us to learn about something when we can't have "the real thing." (The word *simulation* has the same root as "similar." An everyday synonym for "simulate" is "pretend.") So, for the present situation, a simulation is a kind of imitation experiment.

"What's the difference between experimental results and theoretical analysis?"

Ask students to describe the difference between using experimental results and using theoretical analysis to find probability. Try to get them to articulate that although an experiment can give them a feel for what the results might be, it does not guarantee an accurate picture, even with a large number of trials.

"Have you done any simulations in this unit?"

You may want to ask the class if they can think of a problem they worked on earlier in this unit where they did a simulation. If necessary, you can remind them of their experiments for *POW 5: What's on Back?*

• *The one-and-one simulation*

"How would you set up a simulation using these materials?"

Show students the paper bags and the collection of red and yellow cubes, and ask how they might set up a simulation with these materials to study the question in *One-and-One.* If necessary, suggest that they put three red cubes and two yellow cubes in the bag.

"Why is this particular combination of cubes suited to this problem?"

Focus on why this particular combination of cubes is appropriate. Students should see that 60% of the cubes are red, so picking a red cube can represent making a free throw. Picking a yellow cube represents missing a free throw. (Some students may prefer to work with six of one color and four of the other—that's fine.)

Try to have everyone understand that a simulation of a one-and-one free throw situation will go something like this:

> We shake the bag and pull out a cube. If the cube is yellow, the simulation is over, and we write 0 for the score. If the cube is red, we need to draw again to complete the simulation. (Be sure to return the red cube to the bag and shake before drawing again.) If the second cube is yellow, write 1 for the score. If the second cube is red, write 2 for the score.

Go through a few simulations with the class. Then have students work in pairs. Each pair of students should take a bag of cubes and simulate the one-and-one situation 20 times. They should carefully record each result. At the end, they should tally the number of 0's, 1's, and 2's they got.

•*Conclusions from the one-and-one simulation*

Compile a class total of the 0's, 1's, and 2's from the simulations done by the pairs of students, and find the percentage of the time that each score occurred. If the theoretical probabilities are borne out in the experiment, they will have gotten more 0's than any other number. (But don't count on it—2's are a close theoretical second.)

If most students guessed that a score of 1 is the most likely, you may want to ask them to speculate on why they were led astray on this question. (This will be discussed tomorrow, when they will see that the *expected value* per one-and-one situation is very close to 1, even though a score of 1 is actually the *least likely* result.)

You can ask them if they felt the simulation was a good method for analyzing the problem. Tell them that tomorrow they will use an area diagram as a theoretical model to analyze the situation.

Homework 15: A Sixty-Percent Solution
(see facing page)

In this homework, the students do more simulations of the free throw problem done in class. In addition, they begin to think of the problem in terms of expected value.

Homework 15   A Sixty-Percent Solution

In this assignment, the situation is the same as the one described in the activity *One-and-One*.

> Terry is in a one-and-one free-throw situation, and she has a 60% probability of getting any given shot.

Devise some way to simulate the situation at home.

1. Do your simulation of Terry's one-and-one situation 40 times. Describe your method of doing the simulation and record your results.

2. What was the *most frequent outcome* in your simulation?

3. What was the *average score* per one-and-one situation?

Free Throw Analysis

Students do a theoretical analysis of the one-and-one situation.

Mathematical Topics

- Using an area model to investigate the probability of a sequence of events
- More work with expected value

Outline of the Day

In Class

1. Discuss *Homework 15: A Sixty-Percent Solution*
2. *The Theory of One-and-One*
   - Students use an area model to find expected value
3. Discuss *The Theory of One-and-One*
   - Distinguish between *expected value* and *most likely outcome*

- Bring out that the game of Pig is like the one-and-one situation in that both involve a multistage event

At Home

Homework 16: Streak-Shooting Shelly

Discuss With Your Colleagues

Expected Value

The concept of expected value is vital to this unit. This concept, like many others in the IMP curriculum, is not part of a traditional high school mathematics education, and so teachers may be having some difficulty with it.

Teachers can support each other's efforts to learn new mathematics by working through difficult ideas together.

What is your students' understanding of expected value? What is your understanding? How does expected value tie in with "the long run"? Can you separate the general idea from the process for computing it?

1. Discussion of Homework 15: A Sixty-Percent Solution

"What results did you get?"

Ask students to report on their results. Although the great majority of students should have found that Terry's most common result was 0 or 2, most should also see that Terry's average for 40 trials was quite close to 1.

"Can you state the results for Question 3 in terms of expected value?"

Ask students how they could state the results for Question 3 in terms of expected value. They should see that their answers for Question 3 are an experimental estimate of Terry's expected value for each one-and-one situation.

2. The Theory of One-and-One
(see page 120)

Ask students now to work in their groups on the activity *The Theory of One-and-One,* to develop a rug diagram analysis of Terry's expected value. (You may want to begin using the term *area model* instead.)

The method used in this problem will be repeated later in the analysis of Little Pig.

As groups begin work, you may need to give them some hints on how to get started. One useful way to look at this analysis is to consider a convenient number of cases. For example, you can suggest to students that they examine what would happen if Terry faced 100 separate one-and-one situations.

They should be able to see that if Terry's shooting followed the probabilities, she would miss 40 of her first shots and get the other 60.

You may want to suggest that groups start by creating a rug that shows the result of Terry's first shot. Such a rug might look something like this.

40 shots missed	60 shots hit

Note: Students may find it useful to work with grid paper on this problem, using a 10 × 10 section to represent the 100 shots. In that case, the diagram might look like this.

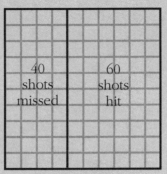

However, if students do use grid paper, you should be aware that later problems may not lend themselves so nicely to whole number solutions, and students should learn to work with more schematic diagrams in which they don't rely on counting squares.

If students need a further hint, you can ask groups to figure out what would happen in the 60 cases in which Terry hit her first shot, and to show this on their diagram. The result might look something like this.

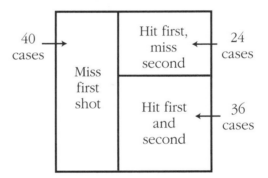

As students work, they may develop and label this final rug in various ways. The following diagram shows another possibility.

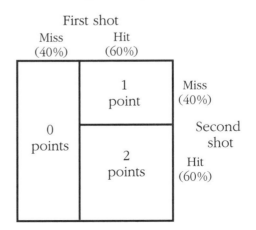

The Theory of One-and-One

You've guessed about it and done simulations about it. Now it's time to work out the theory.

Once again, Terry has a 60% chance of making any given shot.

Develop a theoretical analysis, using a rug diagram, of her expected value for each one-and-one situation.

(A rug diagram is more formally called an **area model**.)

As you circulate around the classroom, you may want to identify one or two groups whose members seem to have a clear understanding of the process and ask them to prepare presentations. You don't need to wait until all the groups have done the analysis.

3. Discussion of
The Theory of One-and-One

Let the heart card member of one or two groups present their work, including diagrams. You may want to go over the arithmetic of finding the portion of the total area for the various sections. For example, if students use a diagram like the last one on page 119, they will need to figure out that the "2 points" section represents 36% of the total area, since it is 60% of 60%. This sort of reasoning can be used in other problems as well.

Students need to identify each section of the rug in terms of both

- the number of cases (or portion of the area) that it represents
- the number of points scored for each case it represents

If the diagram were drawn on a 10 × 10 grid, each box would represent a single one-and-one situation, and students would be able to find areas by counting boxes.

By considering both the number of cases and the point value for each section, students should come up with an analysis that is something like this (based on 100 cases altogether).

- 40 cases worth 0 points each
- 24 cases worth 1 point each
- 36 cases worth 2 points each

Thus, the 100 cases give a total of

$$(40 \cdot 0) + (24 \cdot 1) + (36 \cdot 2) = 96 \text{ points}$$

so the average number of points per one-and-one situation is 0.96. This analysis also confirms that a score of 0 points is the most likely (40% of the time), a score of 2 points is next most likely (36% of the time), and a score of 1 is least likely (24% of the time).

Note: This analysis can be done without use of the rug, just by analyzing what happens in 100 or 1000 cases. But the combination of geometric and arithmetic perspectives is generally helpful for students, and the technique of subdividing cases or area portions will be useful in analyzing the game of Pig.

This is a good time to bring out again that the average result found by this method does not depend on the number of cases tried. For instance, considering a total of 1000 one-and-one situations would give a total of 960 points, resulting in the same average of 0.96 points per one-and-one situation.

• *Expected value versus most likely outcome*

As noted yesterday, students generally think at first that a score of 1 is the most likely result for a one-and-one situation. As the analysis above shows, it is actually the least likely.

"What's the difference between 'expected value' and 'most likely outcome'?"

Help students to understand that the expected value analysis explains this misguided intuition. Although the score of 1 is not the most likely outcome, it is very, very close to the expected value (which is 0.96). So there is something "1-like" about the problem. Stress that there is a danger in confusing the *most likely outcome* with the *expected value*, which is what happens on the average in the long run. Ask students to articulate the difference.

You may want to tell students that "expected average" might be a better phrase for this concept, but that "expected value" has become standard.

• *Multistage events*

"How is the one-and-one situation different from other expected value problems you've looked at?"

Ask how the one-and-one situation was different from other expected value problems. One aspect to bring out is that in the one-and-one situation, the outcome did not happen all at once. In 60% of the cases, there was a second event to consider.

"How does the type of analysis used for the one-and-one situation apply to Pig?"

Ask students how this sort of analysis applies to the game of Pig. They should see that in Pig, a game may consist of one roll of the die or many, and that the number of rolls depends both on what happens on previous rolls and on what decisions the player makes. So students should expect a "subdivided rug" to show up when they analyze Pig.

Homework 16: Streak-Shooting Shelly
(see facing page)

This variation on the one-and-one situation continues students' preparation for the analysis of the game of Little Pig. (Students will start examining that game on Day 22.)

If you think that your students might have difficulty with this assignment, you might give them a hint and suggest that they use a large number of trials and draw an area diagram.

Homework 16   Streak-Shooting Shelly

When Streak-Shooting Shelly steps up for a one-and-one situation, her chances of making the first shot are 80%. However, if she makes her first free throw, then there is a 90% chance that she will make her second free throw.

1. In what percentage of the situations will Shelly score no points? One point? Two points?

2. What is Shelly's expected value per one-and-one situation?

Spins and Draws

Students look at other situations involving expected value.

Mathematical Topics

- Analyzing a situation involving conditional probability by using an area model
- Finding probabilities and expected values for a variety of situations

Outline of the Day

In Class

1. Select presenters for tomorrow's discussion of *POW 6: Linear Nim*
2. Discuss *Homework 16: Streak-Shooting Shelly*
3. *Spins and Draws*
   - Students find expected value in different situations
4. Discuss *Spins and Draws*

At Home

Homework 17: *Aunt Zena at the Fair*

Note: In the follow-up to tomorrow's discussion of tonight's homework, students will be asked to use the random number generator on their graphing calculators. If you are not familiar with how this feature works, you should find out before then.

1. POW Presentation Preparation

Presentations of *POW 6: Linear Nim* are scheduled for tomorrow. Choose three students to make POW presentations, and give them pens and overhead transparencies to take home to use in their preparations.

2. Discussion of *Homework 16: Streak-Shooting Shelly*

"Who's willing to present homework results?"

Ask for volunteers to present their results on the homework problems. (Students may have done the two parts together, as described below, so a second presentation may not be needed other than for variety.)

Emphasize the use of area diagrams for the homework, since they give a visual picture of what is happening, and since such diagrams will be important later in the unit.

The diagrams below are based on a consideration of 100 one-and-one situations. (*Note:* Some students may choose to express diagrams only in terms of percentages, in order to answer Question 1 first, and then convert to cases for Question 2.)

The first diagram shows what happens after one shot.

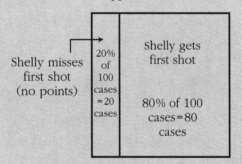

The next diagram subdivides the right-hand area to show what happens on the second shot.

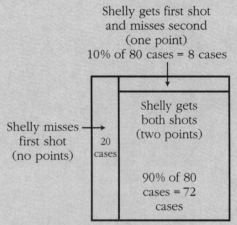

Thus, she gets no points 20 times, one point 8 times, and two points 72 times. (You may want to have students verify that this gives a total of 100 cases.)

In terms of Question 1, the diagram shows that she scores no points 20% of the time, one point 8% of the time, and two points 72% of the time.

For Question 2, students need to look at total points. In terms of the 100 one-and-one situations, Shelly has a total of

$$20 \cdot 0 + 8 \cdot 1 + 72 \cdot 2 = 152 \text{ points}$$

which yields an expected value of 1.52 points per one-and-one situation.

Tell the class that the situation in *Homework 16: Streak-Shooting Shelly* is an example of **conditional probability**, since the probability of Shelly making a free throw depends on when it comes in the shooting sequence. Students will see a more complex example (*Martian Basketball*) on Day 19.

3. *Spins and Draws*
(see next page)

Students will have the rest of the period to work on and report on *Spins and Draws*. When groups have finished Question 1, stop the group work and have the whole class discuss the problem. Then let groups return to Question 2. If time allows, have a discussion as well on Question 2.

4. Discussion of *Spins and Draws*

• *Question 1*

"If you used an area model, how did you divide the area?"

"If you used a large number of trials, how many did you use?"

Have the class compare their methods for tackling the first problem. Here are some questions you might ask about their work on Question 1b.

- If you used an area model, then how did you divide the area?

- If you used a set of trials in which the probabilities worked out perfectly, then how many trials did you use?

There are many ways to make the first problem a fair game. One of the simplest is to change Al's payoff to $1.20 (leaving Betty's payoff at 30¢).

• *Question 2*

In Question 2, there are some tricky parts to look out for. For instance, since the charity gets a penny from each player if neither a jack nor a heart is drawn, the charity gets 2¢ each time it wins.

It is difficult to make an area diagram for this problem, because if the jack of hearts is drawn, both players have to pay and get paid (which means a net gain of 12¢ for Archibald in this case). It might help to draw separate area models for Archibald, for Beatrice, and for the charity, showing what happens to each for different cards.

Spins and Draws

1. Al and Betty are playing spinner games again. This time the spinner is divided up so that the arrow will land in Al's area $\frac{1}{5}$ of the time and in Betty's area the remaining $\frac{4}{5}$ of the time.

   Al pays Betty 30¢ when the arrow lands in her area. Betty pays Al $1.25 when it lands in his area.

   a. What is Al's expected value per spin? What is Betty's?

   b. How might the payments be changed so that the game is fair?

2. Archibald and Beatrice are playing a game that involves drawing a card from a standard deck. After each draw, the card is returned to the deck. (It doesn't matter which person draws the card—all that matters is which card is drawn.)

   If the card drawn from the deck is a jack, then Beatrice pays Archibald 20¢. If the card drawn is a heart, then Archibald pays Beatrice 8¢. If neither a jack nor a heart is drawn, then Archibald and Beatrice each give a penny to charity.

   What is the expected value per draw for Archibald, for Beatrice, and for the charity?

Homework 17   Aunt Zena at the Fair

Aunt Zena has gone to the weekend fair that her nephew's school is running. The school is trying to raise funds so they can offer some special classes.

One of the games that Aunt Zena likes is a ring toss. The goal is to toss a large ring so that it lands on a stick.

Each time Aunt Zena succeeds, she wins a coupon, donated by a local restaurant, for a free dinner. She figures that the coupon is worth about $12. It costs Aunt Zena $1 for each toss.

1. On Saturday when Aunt Zena played this game, she was only able to win about once every 20 tries. (She spent most of the afternoon at the ring toss booth.)

   If she continued like this, would she win or lose money in the long run? (You should consider each coupon she wins as the equivalent of $12.)

   What would be her expected value per toss?

2. Aunt Zena went home that night, determined to do better the next day. She practiced and practiced, and Sunday she went back to the fair. Now she was able to win about once every ten tries.

   If she continued like this, would she win or lose money in the long run? What would be her expected value per toss?

Homework 17:
Aunt Zena at the Fair

This homework assignment is another expected value exercise. Students will use the situation in this assignment tomorrow to learn about the graphing calculator's random number generator.

POW 6 Presentations

Students use their calculators' random number generators to do a simulation. They also present POW 6.

Mathematical Topics

- Simulating a probabilistic situation by using a random number generator
- Finding and generalizing strategies

Outline of the Day

In Class

1. Discuss *Homework 17: Aunt Zena at the Fair*
2. Introduce the calculator's **random number generator**
   - Use the random number generator to simulate the situation in *Homework 17: Aunt Zena at the Fair*
3. Presentations of *POW 6: Linear Nim*
   - Focus on generalizing the strategy

4. Introduce *POW 7: Make a Game*
   - Discuss grading criteria
   - Go over the timetable for the POW

At Home

Homework 18: The Lottery and Insurance—Why Play?

POW 7: Make a Game (final games due Day 32)

Discuss With Your Colleagues

The Role of Peer Evaluation

You may want to have students evaluate each other's games from *POW 7: Make a Game*. Even if you don't do it with POW 7, you may want to consider peer evaluation in some other context.

What are the issues involved in using the grades students give each other as part of their overall course grade? Can students be objective? Are they qualified to make evaluations? How much weight should peer evaluation be given? Should students have a voice in deciding how this matter is handled?

1. Discussion of *Homework 17: Aunt Zena at the Fair*

You can give two groups pens and overhead transparencies for each to prepare a presentation of one of the homework problems. (While these groups prepare, you can have the other groups find Aunt Zena's expected value if she were to win once out of every five tosses, or some other number of their choice.)

When the groups are ready, let spade card students make the presentations. It is very helpful if students use the "large number of trials" method for the problem. Students may handle the arithmetic of Aunt Zena's situation in different ways. We present two possible approaches here, but if students only use one of these (or use some third method), you need not introduce the other approaches.

Suppose, for example, in Question 1, that Aunt Zena plays 600 times (which would take a while). In that case, she wins about 30 times.

One way to compute her net result is to multiply the $12 she wins on each successful toss by 30, and balance this against the $600 she spends in order to play. The arithmetic in this approach might look like 30 • $12 – 600 • $1, which gives a net result of –$240.

Another perspective is to consider that each successful toss gives her a net gain of $11, and each unsuccessful toss represents a loss of $1. From this perspective, her total is found by the expression 30 • $11 + 570 • (–$1). Of course, this also comes out to a net of $ –240.

In either case, Aunt Zena's expected value is –$240 ÷ 600 = –$.40, that is, an average loss of 40¢ per toss.

In Question 2, Aunt Zena has an expected gain of 20¢ per toss.

2. Simulating Aunt Zena's Situation with the Random Number Generator

"How could you simulate Aunt Zena's situation in Question 1?"

The problems in *Homework 17: Aunt Zena at the Fair* provide a good opportunity to introduce the random number facility of the graphing calculator. You might begin by asking the class how they could simulate Aunt Zena's situation in Question 1.

Students might suggest something like putting 20 colored cubes in a bag, with one of them a special color, and drawing out a cube to determine whether she wins or loses on a given toss.

Tell them that their graphing calculator has the capacity to do the same sort of thing. It has a **random number generator**, which will pick a random decimal between 0 and 1. If possible, you should demonstrate the mechanics of how this is done on an overhead viewer.

"How might you use the random number generator to simulate Aunt Zena's situation?"

Ask how they might use the random number generator to simulate Aunt Zena's situation. Try to draw from the class a suggestion such as, "If the number is .05 or less, she wins, and if it's more than .05, she loses." Students should be able to see that this technique is more easily adjusted to different situations than pulling cubes out of a bag or rolling a die. (You may want to mention that on Day 21 they will be writing a calculator program using the random number generator to create a simulation.)

Have students work in pairs, with each pair simulating, say, 40 tosses (or adjust this to fit the numbers used in the homework discussion). That is, they should have the calculator pick a random number 40 times, labeling each result a win or a loss (depending on whether the random number was less than .05 or more than .05) and keeping track of the number of tosses Aunt Zena wins and loses.

As a class, combine results to see if the simulation seems to work, that is, if Aunt Zena does indeed win about $\frac{1}{20}$ of the tosses.

> • *What if the random number is exactly .05?*
>
> Students may raise the question of what to do if the random number is *exactly* .05. If they do not, you might want to bring it up yourself, lest it get in the way later.
>
> Ask them what they think makes sense. One solution is to decide arbitrarily whether .05 will count as a win or a
>
> loss for Aunt Zena. If students are concerned that either choice will be unfair, you can ask what the chances are of getting exactly .05, assuming that the random number generator is truly random and is picking ten-digit decimals. Help students to see that this is a 1-in-10-billion chance, so they shouldn't worry much about it.

3. Presentations of POW 6: Linear Nim

Let the three students make their presentations. The follow-up discussion will depend, as usual, on how complete and clear the presenters were.

It's probably reasonable to expect most students to develop a complete strategy for the original game as described, and you may have some students who develop a more general analysis.

• *A Nim tournament?*

One way to conclude the discussion is with a brief Nim tournament. (You might pick the initial number and maximum per turn, or use the random number generator to do this.)

If students have really understood the game, they should be able to decide almost instantly who will win—the first player or the second—once the game is set up.

4. Introduction of POW 7: *Make a Game*
(see facing page)

You should allow some time for introduction of this POW. In this assignment, students will work *in pairs* to create a game that uses probability and strategy. The pairs will also have to turn in an explanation of how probability and strategy are used in their game.

The following discussion provides some ideas about how you might set up the timing and logistics of this POW. None of the details are written into the student materials, so you can easily make adjustments as you see fit.

• *Creating partnership teams*

There are several methods you can use to create partnership teams. Here are some suggestions.

- Let students find their own partners.

- Assign partners, either by design or at random.

- Assign partners and then let students negotiate changes.

In any case, it is wise to insist that partnerships be firmly decided by the end of tomorrow's class.

• *Turning in preliminary plans*

You should set a date by which students will turn in descriptions of their preliminary ideas for their games. In setting this date, plan to give them some feedback within a couple of days so that teams will have time to do some work on their games before Day 28. We suggest that these preliminary plans be due on Day 22.

You may want to have students from each pair write up their plans individually so that they will each have a record for their portfolios.

• *Day 28: Game workday*

The unit is structured so that Day 28 is largely set aside for students to work on their games. You may want to set up some mechanism on that day that allows students to circulate and get ideas from each other.

As an alternative, you can have students come in to class on Day 28 with "drafts" of their games completed. You can use Day 28 as a "game review" day in which students circulate and comment on each other's games. Students can then revise their games based on the feedback.

• *Day 32: Game day*

Day 32 is designed as a day for students to display and share their final products, and to turn in their final written work on the POW.

You may want to obtain the use of a still camera that day in order to provide photographs of the games that students can add to their portfolios.

POW 7

Make a Game

Working with a partner, you are to invent a game that uses *probability* and *strategy*.

You will need to write very clear instructions so that other people can understand how to play your game. Test your instructions several times with someone at home to make sure that the instructions are easy to follow.

You will also have to turn in a written explanation of how you used ideas about probability and strategy in your game. Your grade on this POW will depend in part on how well you have used such ideas.

• *Grading*

You should discuss the criteria for grading the POW when you introduce the assignment to the class.

We recommend that you involve students in the grading process, in addition to giving your own grades. (You can have students give ratings to each other's games as part of the activities of Day 32.)

If you involve students in the grading process, discuss with them how you will use the grades they give each other in determining their overall grades. They may have misgivings about how this will work, whether they can be fair or critical with each other, and so on.

Point out to students that *you* will also be grading the POW. Emphasize the fact that your grades for them will depend, in large part, on how well they include the mathematical ideas of probability and strategy in their game.

You may want to give students a voice in establishing the grading criteria, especially if they will be involved in the grading process.

Whether or not students help to create the grading criteria, you should be sure that they know what the criteria are, perhaps by posting them or by providing them to students in writing.

Here are some suggested categories for grading.

- *Use of probability:* Students can incorporate probability into their games in several ways.

  They can introduce "real-life" probabilities into the game's rules, to make it believable and realistic.

  They can set up the probabilities in the game to make it more interesting, such as making the chances of winning not too high or too low.

  The game can require *the players* to use probability in some way. For example, the counters game required players to use a strategy based on probability.

- *Use of strategy:* You can use the previous POWs as the basis for a discussion of strategy ideas.

- *Entertainment:* Have students discuss what *they* think makes an entertaining game.

- *Clear instructions:* Have students identify the components of clarity, such as brevity, stating the object of the game, legibility, and covering all possible situations.

- *Overall grade:* Discuss the fact that the final grade should, at least in part, reflect the component grades. It could include a bonus component for imaginative or creative elements, a fancy game board, and so on.

Homework 18   The Lottery and Insurance—Why Play?

This assignment looks at two real-life situations that involve probabilities to see if expected value tells the whole story.

1. *The Lottery*

Many states raise funds through various lottery games. (If your state has one, you may want to learn more about how it works and what happens to the proceeds.)

Continued on next page

Homework 18: The Lottery and Insurance—Why Play?

In this homework, students look at two real-life situations in which probability and expected value play a role. We hope that they will see that having a positive expected value is not always the only consideration in deciding whether or not to "play the game."

Assume that each lottery ticket costs $1. The number of tickets sold and the value of a winning ticket often vary from week to week. Suppose that, for a certain week, about 14 million tickets were sold and that the winning ticket is worth $6 million.

   a. Calculate the approximate expected value of a lottery ticket that week.

   b. Do you think buying a lottery ticket is a wise investment? Explain your answer.

2. *Insurance*

Buying insurance can be thought of as similar to playing a lottery game.

You pay a certain amount, called the *premium,* every month to the insurance company. Most of the time, the insurance company just gets to keep your money, and they pay you nothing.

Sometimes, however, you have a claim that is covered by insurance. When that happens, the insurance company has to pay your expenses (for a car crash, illness, fire, or whatever the incident is), and they generally have to pay you much more in that month than you paid as a premium. So, in a sense, you "win" whenever you collect on your insurance. This means that the "insurance game" is a game that you don't really want to win.

In the long run, insurance companies take in more money in premiums than they pay out in claims, or they wouldn't be in business. In other words, their expected value in the insurance "game" is positive, and yours is negative.

So why do people play?

Martian Basketball

Mathematical Topics

- Seeing the role expected value plays in real-life decisions
- Finding expected value in a three-stage event

Students continue their work with expected value, applying it to more complex situations.

Outline of the Day

In Class

1. Form new random groups
2. Discuss *Homework 18: The Lottery and Insurance— Why Play?*
3. *Martian Basketball*
   - Students examine a variation on the one-and-one situation

- The activity will be discussed on Day 20

At Home

Homework 19: The Carrier's Payment Plan Quandary

1. Forming New Groups

This is an excellent time to place the students in new random groups again. Follow the procedure described in the IMP *Teaching Handbook,* and record the groups and the suit for each student.

2. Discussion of *Homework 18: The Lottery and Insurance—Why Play?*

As a class, discuss the expected value analysis of the lottery question in the homework.

One way to analyze this problem is to use the total of about 14 million tickets sold as the number of trials, and spread out the $6 million payoff equally among the tickets. The average payoff per ticket is about 43¢.

Since the ticket costs $1, this means that on the average, the lottery player loses about 57¢ for each ticket bought. (*Note:* This problem ignores the fact that most lotteries have lots of small payoffs as well as a big prize. Of course, that changes the expected value, but the expected value is still less than the cost of a ticket. The lottery wouldn't be in business if it didn't take in more money than it paid out.)

Discuss the insurance situation briefly to be sure that students understand the general principle that, collectively, people buying insurance get less from the insurance company than they pay in. In other words, *on the average,* people lose money when they buy insurance.

• *Why play?*

"Since the expected value is negative, why would anyone play?"

Then turn to discussion of the larger question in both problems: Why play if the expected value is negative? Let students discuss their reactions to the two situations. There are probably differences of opinion in your class, and your class may not come to a consensus.

In the case of the lottery problem, some students may argue that even though the expected value is negative, the loss of $1 is of no consequence, while the gain of $6 million can radically change one's life. Similarly, in the insurance problem, even though the expected value is negative, it is often the case that people can afford the insurance premium, but cannot afford the possible loss they might incur without insurance, so they consider it worthwhile to "play the insurance game."

• *Zena, the lottery, and insurance*

You may want to ask students what the two situations in last night's homework have in common with Aunt Zena's situation (from *Homework 17: Aunt Zena at the Fair*).

Bring out that in all of these situations, there is an initial outlay by the "player," and then a possible return. In other words, all these situations represent a "pay to play" circumstance, in which the player initially loses money, but may make back some or all of that initial amount, depending on the probabilities involved.

• *Optional: Lottery variations*

If you think your students need more work on these ideas, you might throw in a more complex variation of the lottery problem.

For example, you might tell students that in addition to a 1-in-14-million chance of winning the big prize, a ticket player also has a 1-in-20 chance of winning a smaller prize, such as $5. You can have them compute the expected value per ticket in this modified situation.

Martian Basketball

In Martian basketball, instead of having one-and-one free throw situations, they have one-and-one-and-one situations.

In other words, if a player makes both the first and second shots, then the player can take a third one as well (so the player can get 0 points, 1 point, 2 points, or 3 points).

Suppose our friend Streak-Shooting Shelly moved to Mars and played basketball there.

Shelly still shoots better when she has just made a shot, but her overall quality is down because she is getting adjusted to the different gravity on Mars.

So now she has a 60% probability of making her first shot. If she gets the first one, she has an 80% probability of making the second one, and if she gets the first two, her probability of getting the third is 90%.

1. How many points is she most likely to score in a one-and-one-and-one situation?

2. What is her expected value for each one-and-one-and-one situation?

3. Martian Basketball

This assignment moves the one-and-one situation to another level by including a third shot in the process. Discussion of this activity is scheduled for tomorrow.

Homework 19

The Carrier's Payment Plan Quandary

In some places, newspapers are delivered by a newspaper carrier who has already paid for the papers. The carrier then collects from the customer, and keeps whatever he or she collects.

Suppose one day a customer says to the carrier, "Instead of collecting the usual $5 per week, how about if you just pick two bills at random out of this bag? You get to keep whatever you pick instead of the $5. If you choose to pick out of the bag, you'll do that every week from now on."

Continued on next page

Homework 19:
The Carrier's Payment Plan Quandary

This problem presents a situation in which decision-making is based on expected value. In this problem, the probabilities of the possible outcomes may be somewhat harder for students to find than those in previous problems. (You may want to tell students that a "quandary" is like

• •

The customer shows the newspaper carrier the bag, which contains one $10 bill and five $1 bills. Thus, two sums are possible: $11 and $2. (Of course, the customer will put in new bills each week to replace the ones that were taken the week before.)

You need to figure out if the carrier should take the customer's offer.

1. First, plan and carry out a simulation for a reasonable number of trials. Based on your simulation, decide which is the better choice for the carrier, and explain your decision.

2. Then use an area model or other method to compute the carrier's expected value from the alternative payment plan. That is, find the average the carrier would expect to get per week in the long run using this payment plan. Based on this theoretical analysis, decide which is the better choice, and explain your decision.

3. Which method do you trust more—the simulation or the theoretical analysis—and why?

Adapted from *The Middle Grade Mathematics Project Series: Probability,* by Lappan et al., © 1986 Addison-Wesley Publishing Co., Inc.

a dilemma—that is, a difficult situation in which a decision needs to be made.)

A diagram similar to that used for two-dice sums can be used for this problem, but tomorrow's discussion also describes another method—the *tree diagram*—for analyzing this situation. (Tree diagrams are actually introduced in tomorrow's discussion of today's activity, *Martian Basketball.*)

The situation presented in the activity is one for which you can make up endless variations, as needed.

Tree Diagrams

Mathematical Topics

- Tree diagrams
- Finding probabilities using several methods

Outline of the Day

In Class

1. Discuss *Martian Basketball* (from Day 19)
   - Introduce the use of tree diagrams
2. Discuss *Homework 19: The Carrier's Payment Plan Quandary*

- Use three different approaches:
  area model
  tree diagram
  list of combinations

At Home

Homework 20: A Fair Deal for the Carrier?

Note: We recommend that the class discuss yesterday's activity, *Martian Basketball,* before discussing last night's homework, *Homework 19: The Carrier's Payment Plan Quandary.*

1. Discussion of *Martian Basketball*

As students are settling in, have them compare answers on the activity. Then ask for a volunteer or two to make presentations.

The analysis of this problem is similar to that of *Homework 17: Streak-Shooting Shelly,* but it involves an additional stage. Students may prefer to avoid the use of an area diagram and go straight to a consideration of a convenient number of cases. They will need to use something like

1000 cases in order for the results to come out to whole numbers of cases for each possible outcome.

An area diagram, or series of diagrams, will be helpful to many students in visualizing how each group of results is a fraction of some previous group.

Important: Later in today's discussion, we recommend having students do an analysis of this problem using a tree diagram. But in the analysis of Little Pig, students will primarily be using an area model. So although the tree diagram is an excellent way to think about Shelly's basketball problem, you should insist that the problem be done as well using an area model.

• *Analysis of "Martian Basketball"*

The first two diagrams below are like those for *Homework 16: Streak-Shooting Shelley* (with the percentages changed), and the third diagram demonstrates the overall situation. As before, the diagrams can be expressed in terms of either percentages or cases. These diagrams are based on 1000 cases.

After one shot, the diagram looks like this.

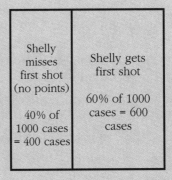

After two shots, the diagram might look like this.

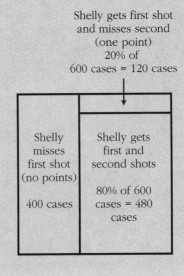

And the final diagram might look like this.

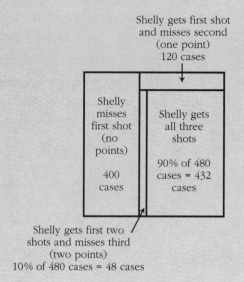

Shelly gets first shot
and misses second
(one point)
120 cases

Shelly
misses
first shot
(no
points)

400
cases

Shelly gets
all three
shots

90% of 480
cases = 432
cases

Shelly gets first two
shots and misses third
(two points)
10% of 480 cases = 48 cases

So, out of 1000 one-and-one-and-one situations, Shelly will hit the first shot 600 times and miss 400 times. The 400 cases where she misses are finished—Shelly gets 0 points in each of these.

Then, of the 600 cases where she makes the first shot, she makes the second shot 80% of the time, for 480 cases, and misses 20% of the time, for 120 cases. These 120 cases are now done—she gets 1 point for each of these.

Finally, of the 480 times when she makes the first two shots, she gets the third shot in 90% of the cases, or 432 times, and misses in 10% of the cases, or 48 times. She gets 3 points for each of the 432 cases and 2 points for each of the 48 cases.

In summary, Shelly's 1000 one-and-one-and-one situations break in this way.

- 3 points: 432 cases

- 2 points: 48 cases

- 1 point: 120 cases

- 0 points: 400 cases

Thus, the most likely result is 3 points (432 cases), while the next most likely result is 0 points (400 cases).

Shelly's point total for 1000 one-and-one-and-one situations is

$$400 \cdot 0 + 120 \cdot 1 + 48 \cdot 2 + 432 \cdot 3 = 1512$$

which gives an expected value of 1.512 points per one-and-one-and-one situation.

Note: If students use, say, 100 cases in all, they will not get a whole number of cases for each possible outcome. If they round off to the nearest whole number, that's fine, as long as they recognize that their answer is approximate.

• *Tree diagram*

Another useful way to describe the possible sequences of events is to use a tree diagram. This method is also suggested for use in today's discussion of *Homework 19: The Carrier's Payment Plan Quandary,* which can serve as a reinforcement of the approach.

If no student introduces something like a tree diagram, you can introduce it one step at a time. Begin by asking what can happen with Shelly's first shot. In response to a student's answer, you can draw a diagram like this.

Hit first shot

Miss first shot

"What happens next?"

Then ask what happens next. Students should be able to articulate that if Shelley misses the first shot, nothing happens, but if she hits the first shot, she takes another one, which she either hits or misses. Gradually, the various ways in which the one-and-one-and-one situation can unfold will appear on the diagram.

You can add the score for each overall outcome to get a diagram like this.

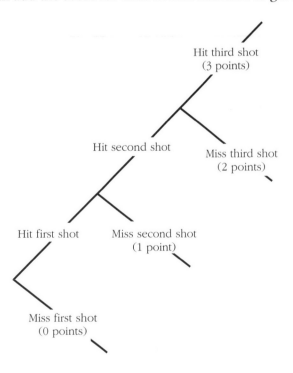

Hit third shot
(3 points)

Hit second shot

Miss third shot
(2 points)

Hit first shot

Miss second shot
(1 point)

Miss first shot
(0 points)

Introduce the term **tree diagram** for this process, and the term **branch** for each segment of the diagram. (We sometimes refer to branches that come off other branches as **subbranches.**)

The numerical information can also be worked out from such a diagram, especially if it is used in coordination with the area diagrams. For example, if students start with 1000 cases, these cases can be portioned out at each stage to the proper branch. At each branching point, the total number of cases coming out is the same as the number of cases going in.

The result should look something like this.

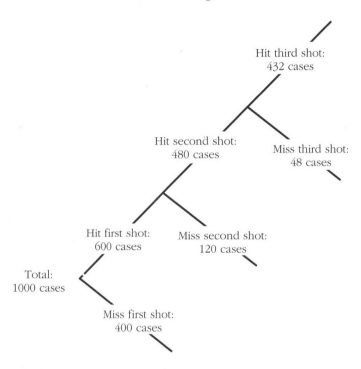

Note: For now, tree diagrams should be thought of primarily as a method for listing and organizing possibilities or sequences of events. At each stage, students can figure out the number of cases for each branch.

In a Year 3 unit, *Pennant Fever*, students will see that they can multiply probabilities as they move out along branches. But understanding that idea requires careful preparation, and students are not expected to learn that in this unit.

2. Discussion of *Homework 19: The Carrier's Payment Plan Quandary*

You can begin the discussion by having groups talk about their methods of simulation and their results. You may want to compile the total results on the board.

The results will probably show an expected value close to $5 per week (which is the theoretical result), so the class will probably not be able to draw any clear conclusions from their simulation about which payment method produces more money for the newspaper carrier.

Keep in mind, however, that for some students, money may not be the deciding factor as to which method is better. Some may argue that the sense of adventure that accompanies the second plan makes it better even if it produces less money in the long run, while others may prefer the security of the first plan, even if it earns less.

• *Theoretical analysis: Three methods*

Now turn to the theoretical analysis. If groups chose to use something other than an area model, that's fine, as long as they can justify their reasoning. There are several ways to explain this problem, but each should lead to the same conclusion.

The notes below present three methods for finding the probability of getting $2 and the probability of getting $11: an area model, a tree diagram, and a list of combinations.

Different students will be comfortable with different methods, and you should work to elicit presentations for each method. In each case we offer suggestions about how to do this.

You should view this discussion as background information that contains suggestions you can use to get students to work the problem through in each of the three methods.

Whichever method is used to find the probabilities, the "large number of trials" method can then be used to get the expected value; see the subheading "Expected value using a large number of trials," which follows the discussion of the three methods.

In discussing the probabilities, you may need to focus on the difference between *possible outcomes* and *equally likely outcomes*. In all of these analyses, each bill is given a name so one can keep track of it. This is helpful in explaining that the probability of drawing a $1 bill is not the same as the probability of drawing the $10 bill, but the probability of drawing a *particular* $1 bill *is* the same as the probability of drawing the $10 bill. In other words, the equally likely events for a given draw are the individual bills, not the amounts.

Many names are possible. We will use T for the $10 bill and O_1, O_2, O_3, O_4, and O_5 for the five $1 bills. If you use this notation, you should take a minute to tell students how to read subscripted variables (for example, "oh sub one") and to explain that this is a common way to represent many variables without using different letters.

• *An area model: First draw, second draw*

Probably the most likely method for students to use is an area model. If no one suggests this, you can ask them how this problem might be done in a way similar to that used for the two-dice sum problem. It may help to think of the bills as drawn one after the other rather than both at once. (This is similar to the use of different colored dice in the two-dice sums analysis.)

In our area model, we begin with a rug with six columns. The six columns would represent the six possibilities for the first bill chosen, and the diagram shows that each is equally likely.

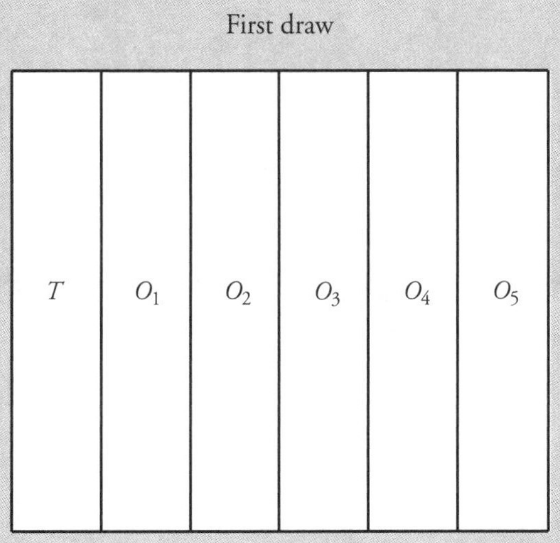

First draw

| T | O_1 | O_2 | O_3 | O_4 | O_5 |

For each possible choice of the first bill, there are five possibilities for the second bill chosen. Thus, each column gets divided into five boxes as shown below. The rug now has 30 equal pieces, which represent equally likely outcomes. The ten shaded boxes show the cases in which a $10 bill and a $1 bill have been drawn, for a total of $11. The 20 unshaded boxes show the cases in which two $1 bills have been drawn, for a total of $2.

First draw

	T	O_1	O_2	O_3	O_4	O_5

Second entry in each box gives second draw	T O_1	O_1 T	O_2 T	O_3 T	O_4 T	O_5 T
	T O_2	O_1 O_2	O_2 O_1	O_3 O_1	O_4 O_1	O_5 O_1
	T O_3	O_1 O_3	O_2 O_3	O_3 O_2	O_4 O_2	O_5 O_2
	T O_4	O_1 O_4	O_2 O_4	O_3 O_4	O_4 O_3	O_5 O_3
	T O_5	O_1 O_5	O_2 O_5	O_3 O_5	O_4 O_5	O_5 O_4

Thus, the probability of drawing $11 is $\frac{10}{30}$ and the probability of drawing $2 is $\frac{20}{30}$. We can represent this symbolically as

$$P(\$11) = \frac{10}{30} = \frac{1}{3} \text{ and } P(\$2) = \frac{20}{30} = \frac{2}{3}$$

Note: Some students may avoid referring to the individual bills by starting with a diagram like this:

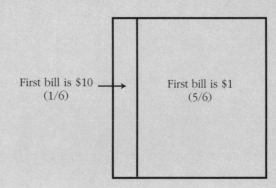

First bill is $10
(1/6)

First bill is $1
(5/6)

and then subdividing the larger section like this:

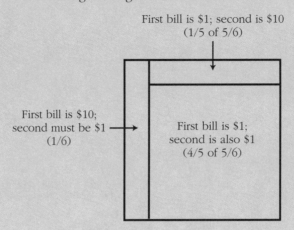

First bill is $1; second is $10
(1/5 of 5/6)

First bill is $10;
second must be $1
(1/6)

First bill is $1;
second is also $1
(4/5 of 5/6)

They can either simplify $\frac{1}{5}$ of $\frac{5}{6}$ and $\frac{4}{5}$ of $\frac{5}{6}$ to $\frac{1}{6}$ and $\frac{4}{6}$ respectively, or work with a convenient number of cases (such as 30) to avoid the arithmetic of fractions.

Note: Another type of diagram for a similar problem is shown on Day 22—see the discussion of *Homework 21: Another Carrier Dilemma.*

• A tree diagram

A tree diagram is an alternative method for finding the probabilities of getting $2 or $11. As noted in today's earlier discussion of *Martian Basketball,* a tree diagram is a method of organizing possible cases, especially in a problem involving a sequence of choices or events. Since students will have been introduced to this method in the earlier discussion, you can simply ask if anyone can do the problem using this method.

They can begin, as we did when using the area model, with the six possibilities for the first bill drawn. But in a tree diagram, these possibilities are shown as branches, rather than as sections of an area diagram.

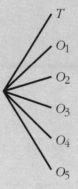

T

O_1

O_2

O_3

O_4

O_5

Then, each of these branches is divided into subbranches that show the possibilities for the second bill. Thus, each of the branches shown above has five subbranches.

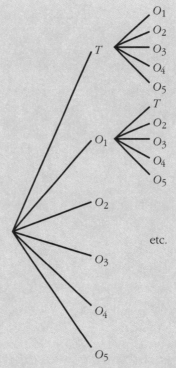

etc.

Since this can get clumsy, it may be preferable to make a separate diagram for each set of subbranches.

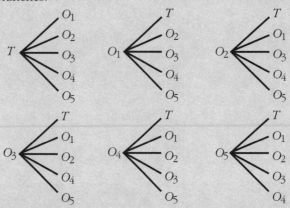

Altogether, there are 30 possible paths, just like the 30 boxes in the area model analysis. Since each of these paths is equally likely, each path has a probability of $\frac{1}{30}$.

Now, as we did with the area model, we can count how many of the paths represent an $11 payment (there are ten: the five paths using the first main branch, and the "top path" from each of the other main branches) and we can count how many represent a $2 payment (the other 20 branches).

Thus, as in the other analyses, $\frac{10}{30}$ of the time the carrier gets $11, and $\frac{20}{30}$ of the time the carrier gets $2.

Reminder. The tree diagrams are being used here to clarify the possible sequences of events, and not as a tool for finding probabilities.

In the example above, all paths were equally likely, so counting the branches of the tree diagram also told us the probabilities; but, as the homework discussion illustrates, other tree diagrams involve distinct probabilities along different branches.

• A list of combinations

In the third method, we generate a list of the possible combinations drawn, without regard to which bill was picked first. You may want to remind students of their work earlier in the unit on *Homework 5: Paula's Pizza*, in which they had to find the total number of possible two-topping pizzas.

If they make a similar list here (using the subscripted names for the individual bills), they might come up with a list like this one.

$$T O_1, \; T O_2, \; T O_3, \; T O_4, \; T O_5$$
$$O_1 O_2, \; O_1 O_3, \; O_1 O_4, \; O_1 O_5$$
$$O_2 O_3, \; O_2 O_4, \; O_2 O_5$$
$$O_3 O_4, \; O_3 O_5$$
$$O_4 O_5$$

Here we have a total of 15 possibilities, of which five combinations give $11, and the other ten combinations give $2. It is important to bring out that these are all equally likely. Although this list can be made into an area diagram, the diagram doesn't really add much to one's understanding, except to represent visually the fact that these are equally likely possibilities.

Thus, the list shows

$$P(\$11) = \tfrac{5}{15} = \tfrac{1}{3} \; \text{ and } \; P(\$2) = \tfrac{10}{15} = \tfrac{2}{3}$$

Fortunately, this approach gives the same result. It is important for students to realize that there are several valid ways to think of the same problem.

Optional: You may want to ask students why they come out with 15 possibilities here, when the other methods showed 30. They may see that the list above ignores the question of *order*. For example, it shows $T O_1$ but does not also show $O_1 T$.

• Expected value using a large number of trials

Whichever method students use to get the probabilities, they then need to find the expected value from the probabilities. They can use the "large number of trials" method, as they did in previous problems.

"With 300 trials, how often would you expect each possible result to occur?"

For example, suppose students choose 300 trials. They should see from the probabilities that the carrier will get $11 about 100 times ($\tfrac{1}{3}$ of the cases) and $2 about 200 times ($\tfrac{2}{3}$ of the cases). Thus, the carrier would expect to get $1,500 for 300 weeks, which is an expected value of exactly $5 a week. In other words, it turns out that the two plans have the same expected value.

"Which plan would you choose, and why?"

After this analysis, you can ask students again to decide which payment plan they would choose and why. Just because the expected value is the same for both plans, it doesn't mean they won't have a preference. For example, some may prefer the alternate plan because it's more exciting, while others like the security of the regular $5 payment.

Homework 20

A Fair Deal for the Carrier?

This problem is a simpler version of the situation in *Homework 19: The Carrier's Payment Plan Quandary*.

As in that situation, the customer would ordinarily pay $5 per week for newspapers.

In this problem, though, the customer places a $20 bill and four $1 bills in a bag, and offers the carrier the option of drawing out just one bill at random.

1. Imagine that you are the paper carrier, and figure out whether this option would give you a better-than-fair deal in the long run. In other words, is the expected value for this option better than the usual $5 per week? Explain how you arrive at your decision.

2. Devise some way to simulate this alternate payment plan, and carry out 20 trials. Find the average result of your trials.

3. Think about how you might write a program for the graphing calculator to do a simulation of the alternate payment plan, and write down any ideas you have about this.

Homework 20: A Fair Deal for the Carrier?

Point out to students that tomorrow they will be writing a program for their graphing calculators to simulate the situation described in this assignment. (That's why tonight's homework uses a simpler version of last night's assignment.)

Calculator Program Simulation

Students write a program on the graphing calculator to simulate the newspaper carrier's situation.

Mathematical Topics

- Programming a simulation on a graphing calculator
- Using a programmed simulation to study expected value

Outline of the Day

In Class

1. Remind students that preliminary POW plans are due tomorrow

2. Discuss *Homework 20: A Fair Deal for the Carrier?*
   - Save the expected value from Question 1 for comparison with results from the graphing calculator simulation

3. Program graphing calculators to simulate the situation in *Homework 20: A Fair Deal for the Carrier?*
   - Review use of the random number generator
   - Develop a general outline, including appropriate variables
   - Turn the outline into a program

   - Enter the program into the calculators
   - Adjust the programs to allow for variation in the number of trials

4. *Using the Programmed Simulation*
   - Students use their program to study the situation in *Homework 20: A Fair Deal for the Carrier?*

5. Discuss *Using the Programmed Simulation*
   - Compare the simulation results to the expected value computed theoretically

At Home

Homework 21: Another Carrier Dilemma

1. Reminder on Preliminary POW Plans

You may want to have students turn in preliminary plans for their POWs tomorrow (see introductory POW discussion on Day 18).

2. Discussion of *Homework 20: A Fair Deal for the Carrier?*

Have a volunteer explain the reasoning used to answer Question 1. The student should find the expected value (probably using the "large number of trials" method) as part of the explanation. Save the result found for the expected value ($4.80) for comparison with the results from the graphing calculator simulation.

You can do an informal poll of students' simulation results before moving on to writing a program for the graphing calculator.

You need not discuss Question 3 explicitly, since students will put their ideas to use as the class goes through the process of developing the program.

3. A Calculator Simulation of a Carrier Problem

Tell students that they are going to write a program for the graphing calculator to simulate the process of drawing a bill out of a bag (as in Question 1 of last night's homework, just discussed). Tell them that the goal is to have the calculator do this process many times (replacing the bill for each new trial) and to keep track to see what happens in the long run. You can suggest that, for now, they should plan to have the calculator do 100 trials. (The discussion below begins with that assumption.)

You can ask them to spend a few minutes in their groups sharing any ideas they had about how they might write the program. You may want to remind them of their work with the random number generator (on Day 18).

• *Using the random number generator*

Begin with a discussion involving the entire class on how to use the random number generator to "pick a bill."

There are various ways to do this. These notes will use a random number between 0 and 0.2 to represent picking the $20 bill and a random number between 0.2 and 1 to represent picking a $1 bill. Whatever method students choose, they should explain how it fits the probabilities of the problem.

Reminder: The issue of what to do if the random number is exactly on the borderline was discussed on Day 18 when the random number generator was used in connection with *Homework 17: Aunt Zena at the Fair.*

You may want to have students try out the random number generator, using an overhead display of the calculator, and to have students keep track on paper of what happens as you use the random number generator repeatedly, say 20 times. Students should see that they need some mechanism in the program, as they do on paper, for recording the results.

• A general outline of the simulation

"What should the calculator do once it picks each random number?"

Ask students to outline how they might have the calculator pick random numbers and keep track of the results as part of a program. You might want to focus specifically on what the calculator should do with each random number it picks.

As was done earlier, you may want to have students briefly discuss this task in small groups before working as a whole class.

Here is one possible outline that might emerge initially.

1. Pick a random number.

2. If the random number is less than 0.2, add $20 to the total amount of money collected so far.

3. If the random number is more than 0.2, add $1 to the total amount of money collected so far.

4. When you've reached 100 trials, do a calculation of the average.

$$\text{average} = \frac{\text{total money received}}{100}$$

• Introducing variables

If students haven't already introduced variables as part of the process, you should suggest that they need to do so. If necessary, review the "labeled storage bin" metaphor for variables in a program (see Day 22 of *Patterns*).

There are many ways in which students might choose variables for this program. One approach uses one variable (we'll use R) to represent the random number, another variable (we'll use T) to represent the total amount of money collected so far, and a third variable (we'll use N) to keep track of the number of trials done so far.

You may need to point out that the statement "when you've reached 100 trials" (in step 4 above) involves another "if" process in the program.

Once variables are introduced, the outline might be expanded to the following:

1. Pick a random number and label it *R*.

2. If *R* is less than 0.2, add $20 to *T*.

3. If *R* is more than 0.2, add $1 to *T*.

4. In either case, add 1 to *N*.

5. If *N* is still less than 100, go back to the beginning and pick another random number.

6. If *N* has reached 100, calculate $\frac{T}{100}$ to get the average collected per trial.

Note: Students may prefer to work in a more verbal and less symbolic form as they write their outline. You should follow their lead as to when and how to include the variables in the outline.

• *Variations in the outline*

Students may choose to record the number of bills picked of each type, rather than the total amount of money collected. This approach would require the use of different variables, and an outline based on this approach might replace steps 2 and 3 with something like this.

2. If *R* is less than 0.2, add 1 to the number of $20 bills picked.

3. If *R* is more than 0.2, add 1 to the number of $1 bills picked.

If students use this approach, they would also need to replace the expression $\frac{T}{100}$ (in step 6) with the expression

$$\frac{20 \cdot (\text{number of \$20 bills}) + 1 \cdot (\text{number of \$1 bills})}{100}$$

Yet another variation might only keep track of the number of $20 bills picked, and use the expression "100 – number of $20 bills" instead of "number of $1 bills" in the final computation.

All of these approaches are fine, and you will have to decide how much time to allow for a discussion of different methods.

• *Turning the outline into a program*

How the class turns the outline into a program will depend on the calculator they use. In particular, you will have to go over the way in which the calculator's programming language deals with "if" statements and with the process of "going back" (**loops**).

There are several details that might be left for students to deal with as the discussion leads into the actual programming.

- They need an **output** step in which the calculator tells the user the answer.

- They may need to **initialize** their variables. That is, they may need to give specific values to some variables at the start of the program. (For example, in the main outline above, both *T* and *N* should start at 0.)

- They may want to make the program "user-friendly" with such additions as having the program say on the screen what the output number represents.

As the program is developed, you or a student can enter it on a display calculator. Then students will need to enter the program into their individual calculators for the next activity, *Using the Programmed Simulation.* If your technology permits, you can transmit the program electronically to individual calculators.

Once the program is entered, let students give it a few practice trials before adding one more detail, varying the number of trials.

> *Suggestion:* You may want to look back at the subsection "Entering the program in a calculator" on Day 22 of *Patterns* for ideas on how to handle the logistics of getting students to enter the program once it's written.

• *Varying the number of trials*

In today's activity, *Using the Programmed Simulation,* students will need to set up the program to use different numbers of trials, rather than 100 trials as was done above. One way to do this is to change the instruction in the program that specifies the number of trials.

Another way is to amend the program so that the number of trials can be varied, chosen by the program user. This will require an **input** step. As with the output, students may want to have the program include information for the user that explains what is being asked for.

4. *Using the Programmed Simulation*
(see next page)

After the program has been written and students have had a chance to play with it, they should work on the activity *Using the Programmed Simulation* to investigate how changing the number of trials affects the results.

You may want to suggest that each group use one of its calculators to do a very large number of trials, like 10,000, while the group tries smaller simulations on other machines.

Students will probably have an intuitive understanding of the activity's main idea, which is that the larger the number of trials, the more reliable the simulation. You might mention that with the extremely fast computers available today, simulation can be a valuable tool for the evaluation of many situations.

> *Note:* Later in the unit, you might provide students with the opportunity to do another simulation, this time on a computer, to test and evaluate strategies for the game of Pig and a variation called Little Pig. (Little Pig is introduced on Day 22.) In that simulation, they will be able to play millions of games in just minutes.

Using the Programmed Simulation

Now that you have a calculator program that simulates the situation of *Homework 20: A Fair Deal for the Carrier?*, it's time to see what you can learn from that program.

1. Run the program several times using the same number of trials. How do your answers for the expected value vary from one run to the next? How do they compare to the theoretical prediction?

2. Now do several runs with a larger number of trials, and again compare your answers to each other and to the theoretical prediction. How are these results different from the results in Question 1?

3. What conclusions can you draw about the influence of the number of trials on the results?

4. Does your calculator simulation give you more confidence in the theoretical analysis? Explain.

5. Discussion of *Using the Programmed Simulation*

Only a brief discussion is needed, to compare students' results from their simulation to the theoretical expected value. If the results are not close, you might have students speculate about why they are not.

Homework 21

Another Carrier Dilemma

Here is one more variation on the newspaper carrier's situation. This time the customer places two $5 bills and three $1 bills in a bag, and allows you to draw out two of the bills at random.

If you use this method week after week, how much would you expect to get, on the average, in the long run?

Explain your reasoning for this problem using more than one method of analyzing the situation.

Homework 21:
Another Carrier
Dilemma

This assignment focuses on the different approaches to finding the probabilities of the different possible outcomes.

Days 22–25

Little Pig

This page in the student book introduces Days 22 through 25.

In *One-and-One*, Terry took at most two shots at the basket in each one-and-one situation. In *Martian Basketball*, each "turn" involved at most three shots.

In the game of Pig, there is no limit to how long a turn can last. A person could roll 20, 50, even 100 times without getting a 1 on the die, continuing to accumulate more points. This is one reason why the game is so complicated to analyze.

You have one more task before you return to finding the best strategy for Pig, and that is to look at a simplified version of the game, called Little Pig. You'll play around for a little while to get used to this new game, and then you'll start analyzing strategies by using area diagrams.

Edward Rokos prepares his analysis of "Little Pig."

Little Pig

Mathematical Topics

• Devising strategies for the game of Little Pig

Outline of the Day

In Class

1. Collect preliminary POW plans

2. Discuss *Homework 21: Another Carrier Dilemma*

3. *The Game of Little Pig*
   • Students are introduced to a simpler version of the game of Pig

4. Discuss *The Game of Little Pig*
   • Students share strategies

At Home

Homework 22: Pig Tails

Special Materials Needed

• A bag for each group containing a blue, a yellow, and a red cube (or equivalent)

1. Collection of Preliminary POW Plans

You may want to collect students' preliminary plans for *POW 7: Make a Game* today. Keep in mind that Day 28 is set aside for students to work on these games, so you will probably want to give students feedback on their plans before then.

2. Discussion of Homework 21: Another Carrier Dilemma

You may want to start with one volunteer and then ask for other volunteers who used different methods. If possible, find students who used each of the three methods presented in the discussion of *Homework 19: The Carrier's Payment Plan Quandary*—an area model, a tree diagram, and a list of combinations. The main focus should be on finding the probabilities for each outcome, because finding the expected value once the probabilities are known should be fairly routine by now.

• A different area diagram

Since one purpose of this activity is to provide students with a variety of approaches, we show below a slightly different type of area diagram from that used on Day 20 for *Homework 19: The Carrier's Payment Plan Quandary.* Here, the diagram shows all the possible bills along both the top and the side, and shades out the impossible cases that would represent the same bill being drawn twice. The number in each box shows the total amount of money the carrier gets.

The two $5 bills are labeled F_1 and F_2 and the three $1 bills are labeled O_1, O_2, and O_3.

First draw

	F_1	F_2	O_1	O_2	O_3
F_1		$10	$6	$6	$6
F_2	$10		$6	$6	$6
O_1	$6	$6		$2	$2
O_2	$6	$6	$2		$2
O_3	$6	$6	$2	$2	

Second draw

Since there are 20 possible cases, one can determine by counting boxes that the probability of getting $10 is $\frac{2}{20}$, the probability of getting $6 is $\frac{12}{20}$, and the probability of getting $2 is $\frac{6}{20}$.

Students' description of the two other approaches—the tree diagram and the list of combinations—will probably be quite similar to the descriptions of these two approaches given on Day 20 for *Homework 19: The Carrier's Payment Plan Quandary.*

• The expected value

For your convenience: If the carrier accepts the customer's alternate payment plan, the expected value per week can be found by using this computation (using 100 weeks as the "long run").

$$\frac{10 \cdot 10 + 60 \cdot 6 + 30 \cdot 2}{100}$$

This comes out to $5.20 per week.

3. *The Game of Little Pig*

(see next page)

The game of Little Pig is very similar to the game of Pig played at the beginning of the unit, but it is simple enough that area models for many common strategies can be constructed by the students.

You can introduce the game by explaining to students that, theoretically, they could use area diagrams and the concept of expected value to compare different strategies for Pig. But unfortunately, an analysis of Pig strategies gets very complicated very quickly.

Tell them that, because of this, the unit will help them discover another way to think about how to find the best strategy. To find this other approach, they will work for the next several days with a somewhat simpler game, called Little Pig, and analyze several strategies using area diagrams.

For clarity, from now on we will sometimes refer to the original game of Pig as "Big Pig." You should introduce this new name because it is used in some student materials.

After analyzing many individual strategies for Little Pig, students will look at how to find the best possible strategy. They will then apply these insights in order to find the best strategy for Pig itself without having to draw the messy diagrams.

Today's work with Little Pig is just exploratory. Let students play for a while, and then ask them to think about possible strategies as they play.

As with *Pig Strategies* on Day 2, you can have each group put its strategy on a sentence strip, for display during the discussion.

Note: Instead of using colored cubes, students can use the random number generator on their graphing calculators.

The Game of Little Pig

The game of Little Pig is similar to the game of Pig that you have already played.

To play Little Pig, you need a bag containing three cubes—one red, one blue, and one yellow.

Instead of rolling a die, as you did in the game of Pig, you will draw a cube out of the bag.

In each turn, you can draw as many times as you want (replacing the cube after each draw), until either you decide to stop or you draw a yellow cube. Each time you draw a red cube, you add one point to your score. Each time you draw a blue cube, you add four points to your score.

If you stop drawing before you draw a yellow cube, your score for that turn is the total number of points for all draws in that turn. But if you draw a yellow cube, the turn is over and your score for that turn is zero.

Your eventual goal will be to find a strategy for Little Pig that will give the highest possible average score per turn in the long run. In other words, you want the strategy with the highest possible expected value per turn.

For now, you will just be informally investigating the game.

1. Play the game several times in your group, noting different possible strategies.

2. Make a list of some possible strategies for playing Little Pig.

3. Choose a single group strategy that you think might give the best results. Be sure to write this strategy clearly.

4. Discussion of *The Game of Little Pig*

Spend some time having each group share a possible strategy with the whole class. Be sure that these strategies are clearly stated.

If you still have the sentence strips posted from *Pig Strategies,* you might want to ask students to look at how these strategies compare.

If time allows, have groups play some games using another group's strategies. You need not gather any data on the results of the strategies.

You may want to have students find the expected value for the strategy of stopping after the first cube is drawn no matter what the result. Working through this simple example may help with tonight's homework.

Melissa Maloney takes notes on the presentation of a fellow student

Homework 22

Pig Tails

The game of Pig Tails is another variation on the game of Pig. Here's how you play.

Each turn consists of flipping a coin until either you decide to stop or you get tails. If you stop before getting tails, your score for the turn is the number of heads you got, that is, the number of times you flipped.

But if you get tails before deciding to stop, your score for the turn is zero.

1. What is your expected value per turn if your strategy is to flip just once and then stop (no matter what the result)?

2. Next, consider the strategy of always flipping twice (unless you get tails on the first flip) and then stopping. What is your expected value for this strategy?

3. What is the expected value per turn if you always flip three times (unless you get tails on the first or second flip)?

4. Generalize Questions 1 through 3. That is, find the expected value per turn if your strategy is to flip n times and then stop (unless you get tails on an earlier flip).

Homework 22:
Pig Tails

This expected value problem sets up a pattern of results for students to generalize.

DAY 23

Little Pig Analysis Begins

Students begin analyzing Little Pig strategies by using area diagrams.

Mathematical Topics

- Using an area model analysis to find the expected value for strategies for Little Pig

Outline of the Day

In Class

1. Discuss *Homework 22: Pig Tails*
   - (Optional) Consider the cost of an extra flip to see why one should stop after two flips

2. *Little Pig Strategies*
   - Students use an area model to find the expected value for two simple strategies for Little Pig

3. Discuss *Little Pig Strategies*
   - Find expected values and compare the strategies
   - Post expected values and diagrams for comparison with other strategies

At Home

Homework 23: Continued Little Pig Investigation

Note: It is hard to predict how much time your students will need for the analysis of various Little Pig strategies, although a total of three days seems typical. Once students get going on this analysis, they generally are ready to keep on with more examples.

The homework assignments for Days 23 and 24 are written in a very general way so that you can adapt them to your needs.

The outline below shows what might occur in the classroom, but you may find that you need to vary from this schedule.

Day 23: After discussing *Homework 22: Pig Tails,* students work on and discuss *Little Pig Strategies* and get started on the 3-draw diagram in class; for *Homework 23: Continued Little Pig Investigation,* you might have them complete the 3-draw strategy and also do the 3-point strategy.

Day 24: Students discuss their work on the 3-draw and 3-point strategies, and compare these to the 2-draw and 2-point strategies; they continue the analysis in class, perhaps completing either the 4-point or 4-draw strategy; for *Homework 24: Even More Little Pig Investigation,* you can have them finish the 4-point and 4-draw cases or start on more complex examples.

Day 25: Students share their homework results, and continue to work through at least the 5-point strategy; they are told the results for some further strategies, and speculate about the optimal strategy; for homework, they do *Homework 25: Should I Go On?*

1. Discussion of *Homework 22: Pig Tails*

Have students share their homework results in their groups and come up with a group consensus. You might choose one group at random to present their solution to Question 1, another group for Question 2, and a third for Question 3. Let club card students from these groups present the group's consensus. You can have other students add further ideas as the presentations are made.

Be sure that everyone understands the solution to Question 1 before moving on. It should be clear to all that with the one-flip strategy, you will get one point half the time and no points half the time, so the average score is $\frac{1}{2}$.

On Question 2, students should see that the only way to get a non-zero score is to get two heads in a row, and that this happens $\frac{1}{4}$ of the time, giving two points each time it happens. (See the Day 8 discussion of Question 3 in *Homework 7: Portraits of Probability.* You can review the diagram used there if needed.)

Based on that probability, students should be able to see (perhaps by using the "large number of games" approach) that the expected value is again $\frac{1}{2}$.

On Question 3, if needed, ask:
"What is the probability of getting a non-zero score?"
"How many points do you get when you get a non-zero score?"

On Question 3, you can help if needed by focusing the discussion on two points.

• What is the probability of getting a non-zero score?

• How many points do you get when you get a non-zero score?

Students should see that a non-zero score requires three heads in a row, and yields a score of three points. Students should be able to see (perhaps using an area diagram) that the probability of getting three heads in a row is $\frac{1}{8}$.

Students should then see that if you get three points on $\frac{1}{8}$ of your turns and no points the rest of the time, your average score per turn is $\frac{3}{8}$.

Discussion of the generalization (Question 4) is optional. You can pursue this if students have ideas, but it isn't necessary that they get the general solution.

For your information: For a strategy of flipping n times, the only way to get a non-zero score is to flip n heads. The probability of doing this is $\frac{1}{2^n}$ and the score for a sequence of n heads is n. Thus the expected value per turn for an n-flip strategy is $\frac{n}{2^n}$, which is $\frac{1}{2}$ if $n = 1$ or $n = 2$, and then gets smaller as n increases.

Optional: Cost of the next flip

Students' understanding of how to find the best strategy for the Big Pig and Little Pig games may be helped if you pose this question about Pig Tails.

> Suppose you walk into a room where your friend is in the middle of a game of Pig Tails. Your friend has to leave and asks you to finish the game. Your friend has gotten four heads so far this game.
>
> Do you flip again or not?

Ask students to imagine that this scenario is going to be repeated over and over, and that their goal is to do as well as possible for their friend *in the long run*.

The key idea is to see that another flip can either gain them one point or cost them four points. Since these two outcomes are equally likely, it will be a losing proposition in the long run to flip again.

Note: Students will do similar comparisons of strategies at various points in this three-day sequence. This will culminate (for Little Pig) in *Homework 25: Should I Go On?* They will then do something similar in *Homework 26: Big Pig Meets Little Pig*.

So you should recognize that this is just the first of several looks at the "should I go on?" idea and you need not expect full comprehension from students at this point.

2. *Little Pig Strategies*
(see next page)

Tell students that today they will analyze some Little Pig strategies by using the idea of expected value. Though the area model analyses of some Little Pig strategies are more complex than the analyses of the one-and-one problems or the newspaper carrier problems, these analyses use the same general approach that was used in those problems.

Let students work on the activity *Little Pig Strategies*. You may want to have some groups start on the 2-draw strategy and others start on the 2-point strategy, and stop the groups when they have all done at least their first problem. You can give a transparency for each problem to one group that has successfully worked through that problem.

Suggestion: Students may find their work on earlier problems to be helpful in thinking about the multistage problems involved in analyzing Little Pig

Little Pig Strategies

Now that you have gotten some experience playing Little Pig, it's time to analyze some strategies.

Two strategies are described below. For each strategy, use an area diagram to describe what might happen and to find the expected value per turn if you play using that strategy.

1. *The 2-Point Strategy*

In this strategy, you stop as soon as you have at least two points. (Of course, if you draw a yellow cube before getting two points, you'll have to stop sooner.)

2. *The 2-Draw Strategy*

In this strategy, you stop after drawing two cubes, no matter what the results of those two draws. (Of course, if the first cube is yellow, you'll have to stop after only one draw.)

strategies. Day 16's activity, *The Theory of One-and-One,* and Day 19's *Martian Basketball* are particularly relevant.

3. Discussion of *Little Pig Strategies*

Let the groups present their work, which should be quite similar to the analysis of the one-and-one problems. You should start with the 2-point strategy, since the diagram for that is slightly simpler.

• *The 2-point strategy*

Be sure that the group shows the development of its area diagram and not just the final result, and that they explain what each section represents

Students are likely to start with a diagram that is something like this to show the possible results after one draw.

sure they clarify why the other sections don't get subdivided.)

This would lead to a second diagram that might look like this.

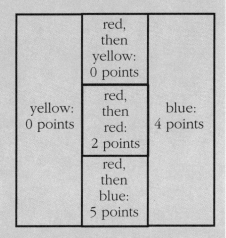

They are then likely to explain that in the case of a red cube on the first draw, you would draw again, since you don't have two points yet. (Be

This diagram shows a complete set of possibilities for the 2-point strategy, with each section showing the number of points for a particular sequence of draws.

It is crucial that students see that although there are four possible outcomes (0 points, 2 points, 4 points, or 5 points), these outcomes are not equally likely. In fact, the five boxes that are shown above are not equally likely either, since two of them are larger than the rest.

"What is the probability of each of four possible scores?"

To get at this idea, ask the students what the probability is of each of four outcomes or for each of the five boxes. If students have trouble seeing that the smaller boxes are each $\frac{1}{9}$ of the total, one helpful approach is to mentally subdivide each of the long rectangles into three sections in order to get equal areas.

Here are the probabilities.

- P(0 points) = $\frac{1}{3} + \frac{1}{9} = \frac{4}{9}$

- P(2 points) = $\frac{1}{9}$

- P(4 points) = $\frac{1}{3}$

- P(5 points) = $\frac{1}{9}$

Note: It may be clearer if students write $\frac{1}{3}$ as $\frac{3}{9}$ so they can compare the probabilities more easily and so that it's obvious that the fractions add up to 1.

Discuss how to go from the probabilities or the diagram to finding the expected value, preferably by using the "large number of trials" approach. You may want to discuss how to choose a convenient number of trials, based on the fact that the sections of the diagram represent thirds and ninths.

Using 900 trials, this is how the cases would break down.

- Yellow on first draw: 300 cases

- Red, then yellow: 100 cases

- Red, then red: 100 cases

- Red, then blue: 100 cases

- Blue on first draw: 300 cases

(You can have students verify that this totals 900 cases.)

Students may prefer to list the cases by score rather than color sequence.

- 0 points: 400 cases

- 2 points: 100 cases

- 4 points: 300 cases

- 5 points: 100 cases

Using the latter breakdown gives this expression for the expected value.

$$\frac{(400 \cdot 0) + (100 \cdot 2) + (300 \cdot 4) + (100 \cdot 5)}{900}$$

(Of course, students may choose to omit the term that is zero.)

This yields an expected value of $\frac{1900}{900}$. This simplifies to $2\frac{1}{9}$, which is approximately 2.11.

Post this expected value of 2.11 and an area diagram to explain the result, and post similar information for subsequent strategies. Comparison of one strategy with another—in terms of both the expected values and the diagrams—will be important in finding the best strategy. These theoretical results can also be compared with the results from the computer simulation (see Day 26).

Comment: In the 2-point strategy, the player gets a score below average most of the time (500 out of 900 scores are below average). A similar result is true for almost all of the strategies analyzed for Little Pig. You may want to point this out to students and ask them to ponder this apparent paradox. A discussion of this phenomenon will clarify the distinction between mean and median.

• *The 2-draw strategy*

The analysis for the 2-draw strategy will be similar, except that the section representing a blue cube on the first draw must also be subdivided.

Post the diagram and the expected value of 2.22 for the 2-draw strategy.

The final area diagram of the 2-draw strategy should look something like this.

yellow: 0 points	red, then yellow: 0 points	blue, then yellow: 0 points
	red, then red: 2 points	blue, then red: 5 points
	red, then blue: 5 points	blue, then blue: 8 points

Using 900 cases here as well, this is how they would break down.

- Yellow on first draw: 300 cases
- Red, then yellow: 100 cases
- Red, then red: 100 cases
- Red, then blue: 100 cases

- Blue, then yellow: 100 cases
- Blue, then red: 100 cases
- Blue, then blue: 100 cases

If students list the cases by score, they should get this breakdown.

- 0 points: 500 cases
- 2 points: 100 cases
- 5 points: 200 cases
- 8 points: 100 cases

Using the list by score, the computation for expected value becomes

$$\frac{(500 \cdot 0) + (100 \cdot 2) + (200 \cdot 5) + (100 \cdot 8)}{900}$$

which yields an expected value of $\frac{2000}{900}$. This simplifies to $2\frac{2}{9}$, which is approximately 2.22.

• *Comparing the strategies*

Comparing these two strategies gives a taste of how one can find the best strategy. Students presumably will see that the 2-draw strategy yielded a higher expected value than the 2-point strategy.

"How come the two strategies give different expected values?"

Ask students to explain where the difference in the strategies showed up in the analysis, and why it worked in favor of the 2-draw strategy.

Help them as needed to see that the only difference in play occurs if the first cube is blue. With the 2-point strategy, one stops, while with the 2-draw strategy, one draws again. The practical result of drawing again, in terms of the 900-case analysis, is to replace 300 4-point games with 100 0-point games, 100 5-point games, and 100 8-point games.

Thus, students should see that they are better off with an equal mixture of 0's, 5's, and 8's than they are with all 4's.

Another way to express this is to say that since the average of 0, 5, and 8 is more than 4, drawing after a blue cube gives an improvement in the expected value.

Without forcing the issue, try to get students to see that this means that if you draw blue on your first cube, you're better off drawing again than stopping. A more careful look at this type of reasoning will be the ultimate basis for finding the best strategy and explaining why it is best.

Homework 23: Continued Little Pig Investigation
(see facing page)

For homework, you might have students analyze the 3-draw and 3-point strategies.

If possible, have students get started in class on the 3-draw strategy, since the diagram for this is one stage more complicated than those that students have done so far.

If students are further along, you can assign a 4-point or 4-draw strategy for homework. If they are moving more slowly, you can have them finish their work on the 2-draw and 2-point strategies for homework.

You may want to ask students to analyze one other strategy of their choice, not necessarily restricting them to "point" and "draw" strategies.

Homework 23

Continued Little Pig Investigation

At this point, you have found the expected value for some Little Pig strategies.

Your task in this assignment is to continue this investigation. You will either use strategies of your own choice or you will be assigned specific strategies to investigate by your teacher.

DAY 24

Little Pig Analysis Continues

Students continue their analysis of Little Pig strategies.

Mathematical Topics

- Using an area model analysis to find the expected value for strategies for Little Pig

Outline of the Day

In Class

1. Discuss *Homework 23: Continued Little Pig Investigation*
   - Compare the 3-point strategy to the 2-point strategy
   - Compare the 3-draw strategy to the 2-draw strategy
   - Post expected values and diagrams for comparison with other strategies

2. Continue work on Little Pig strategies
   - Analyze the 4-point strategy
   - Analyze other strategies as time allows
   - Post expected values for all new strategies

At Home

Homework 24: Even More Little Pig Investigation

1. Discussion of *Homework 23: Continued Little Pig Investigation*

Whatever strategies students worked on for homework, you can begin the day by having some volunteers share their results. The following discussion is based on the expectation that students will have analyzed the 3-draw and

3-point strategies for homework. For your convenience, we include possible final area diagrams for each of these strategies.

Reminder: Post the diagram and expected value for each new strategy discussed.

• *The 3-point strategy*

The only change needed from yesterday's analysis of the 2-point strategy is that the "red, then red" section of that diagram has to be subdivided, giving a diagram like this.

yellow: 0 points	red, then yellow: 0 points	blue: 4 points
	r, r, y: 0	
	r, r, r: 3	
	r, r, b: 6	
	red, then blue: 5 points	

The expected value for the 3-point strategy is $2\frac{2}{9}$, which is approximately 2.22. (Students may find it convenient to use 27 trials, since the smallest section represents $\frac{1}{27}$ of the total area.)

Have students compare this with the 2-point strategy discussed yesterday. (This is similar to yesterday's comparison of the 2-draw and 2-point strategies.)

Help them to see that the 3-point strategy is better than the 2-point strategy because the 3-point strategy replaces the "red, then red" section, where the score is 2 points, by equal-sized sections worth 0, 3, and 6 points. Students should see that they are better off with an equal mixture of 0's, 3's, and 6's than they are with all 2's.

• *The 3-draw strategy*

For the 3-draw strategy, students have to subdivide those sections from yesterday's 2-draw strategy that don't already have a yellow cube drawn, giving a diagram like this.

	red, then yellow: 0 points	blue, then yellow: 0 points
yellow: 0 points	r, r, y: 0	b, r, y: 0
	r, r, r: 3	b, r, r: 6
	r, r, b: 6	b, r, b: 9
	r, b, y: 0	b, b, y: 0
	r, b, r: 6	b, b, r: 9
	r, b, b: 9	b, b, b: 12

The expected value for this strategy is also $2\frac{2}{9}$, which is the same as the expected value for both the 2-draw and 3-point strategies.

Ask students to compare this diagram with yesterday's diagram for the 2-draw strategy to see how they differ and what they might learn from the comparison. This time there are several ways in which the two strategies being compared are different.

Students should see that the 2-draw strategy's "red, then red" box (worth 2 points) is replaced here by equal-sized boxes worth 0, 3, and 6 points, so this is an improvement, from 2 points to an average of 3 points. But the 2-draw strategy's "blue, then blue" box (worth 8 points) is replaced by equal-sized boxes worth 0, 9, and 12 points, and this is a change for the worse, from 8 points to an average of 7 points. The other two boxes that are altered have no net change in average score, and, overall, the 2-draw and 3-draw strategies have the same expected value.

Note: Do not push students to generalize about when it pays to subdivide the box. That is a big step, and it will be the focus of *Homework 25: Should I Go On?*

• *Other types of strategies*

If students analyzed anything other than "point" or "draw" strategies for homework, have them present their results now, and compare them with the other strategies considered so far.

• *Summary so far*

If you haven't yet done so, add the expected value results for the strategies analyzed today to your posted list begun yesterday. Your list should now include at least the following information:

- 2-point strategy: expected value = $2\frac{1}{9} \approx 2.11$

- 2-draw strategy: expected value = $2\frac{2}{9} \approx 2.22$

- 3-point strategy: expected value = $2\frac{2}{9} \approx 2.22$

- 3-draw strategy: expected value = $2\frac{2}{9} \approx 2.22$

Take a minute to look over the strategies analyzed so far and identify the best expected value yet achieved.

Then ask students to continue their analysis, trying to find one that's even better. Review the fact that the goal is to find the strategy for Little Pig with the best expected value.

It may be of help to identify the two general types of strategies discussed so far:

- "Point" strategies, in which you stop as soon as you reach a certain preset number of points

- "Draw" strategies, in which you stop after a certain preset number of draws

2. Continued Work on Little Pig Strategies

For the rest of today's class, students should be allowed to continue their investigations in their own way, trying other strategies and thinking about why one is better than another. You can use this opportunity to solidify the method of analysis for students who may be somewhat confused.

Generally speaking, you may expect that today students will finish the discussion of the 3-draw and 3-point strategies, make some comparisons and summarize their work so far, and then perhaps analyze the 4-point strategy in class.

For your convenience: The expected value for the 4-point strategy is $2\frac{20}{81}$, which is approximately 2.247.

Homework 24 · · · · · Even More Little Pig Investigation

Again, your task in this assignment is to continue the investigation of different strategies for Little Pig.

As you work, keep in mind the ultimate goal of finding the strategy with the largest possible expected value per turn.

Homework 24: Even More Little Pig Investigation

Assuming that students have completed the analysis of the 4-point strategy, you can have them analyze the 4-draw and 5-point strategies for homework. You can suggest to ambitious students that they push the process even further.

Little Pig Analysis Continues Further

Students continue their analysis of Little Pig strategies.

Mathematical Topics

- Using an area model analysis to find the expected value for strategies for Little Pig

Outline of the Day

In Class

1. Discuss *Homework 24: Even More Little Pig Investigation*

2. Continue work on Little Pig strategies
   - Consider giving students the expected values for other "point" and "draw" strategies

3. Have students examine their results and draw some conclusions

At Home

Homework 25: Should I Go On?

1. Discussion of Homework 24: Even More Little Pig Investigation

As was done yesterday, have students present their results on the strategies they analyzed for homework.

For your convenience: Here are the results for the 4-draw and 5-point strategies.

- 4-draw strategy: expected value = $1\frac{79}{81} \approx 1.975$
- 5-point strategy: expected value = $2\frac{88}{243} \approx 2.362$

2. Continued Work on Little Pig Strategies

After presenting their results, students can continue analyzing more strategies. Use your judgment about how far to have students go with this. At some point, you may want to interrupt and simply give them some further results.

For your convenience: Here are the expected values for some other "point" and "draw" strategies.

- 5-draw strategy: expected value = $1\frac{157}{243} \approx 1.646$

- 6-point strategy: expected value = $2\frac{88}{243} \approx 2.362$

- 6-draw strategy: expected value = $1\frac{231}{729} \approx 1.317$

- 7-point strategy: expected value = $2\frac{710}{2187} \approx 2.325$

3. Comparing Results

Once students have accumulated a good collection of results, tell them to stop any further analysis of strategies and to look at what they have.

"What appears to be the best strategy?"

Students may see that the "draw" strategies are getting worse as the number of draws increases, which may suggest to them that one of the "point" strategies is best. They may also see (if they get this far) that the 7-point strategy is not as good as the 6-point strategy, which suggests that continuing to draw beyond seven points is not worthwhile.

It turns out that the 5-point and 6-point strategies both yield the maximum possible expected value, and no other strategy is as good.

A diagram for the 5-point strategy might look like this:

yellow: 0 points	red, then yellow: 0 points	blue, then yellow: 0 points
	r, r, y: 0 pts 0 | 0/5/8 | 7 r, r, b: 6 pts	blue, then red: 5 points
	red, then blue: 5 points	blue, then blue: 8 points

where the small boxes in the middle come from the following color sequences:

r, r, r, y: 0 points	r, r, r, r, y: 0 points	r, r, r, b: 7 points
	r, r, r, r, r: 5 points	
	r, r, r, r, b: 8 points	

• For teachers: Points versus draws and the gambler's fallacy

One of the key ideas that should come out of this discussion is that the best strategy is "points-based." That is, in the best strategy, the decision about whether or not to draw again should depend only on how many points one has so far, not on the number of rolls or the particular sequence that led to that total. (More details on this analysis are in the Day 26 discussion of *Homework 25: Should I Go On?*, especially in the subsection "Does it matter how they got there?")

This conclusion is due to the fact that we are defining "best" in terms of expected value and that we are assuming that the probabilities are the same for every draw. An expected value analysis of what to do in a given situation involves looking at how much you might lose and how much you might gain by a given action, and the probabilities of each possible result. How a player got to a given point score does not affect the amount that is at risk. In Pig and its variations, the number of draws you had before does not affect the probability of what will happen now. Students should be moving toward this conviction.

The fact that the optimal strategy is "points-based" may surprise many students (as it surprises many adults, even if they are mathematically sophisticated). The common desire to work with a "draws-based" strategy may have something to do with the gambler's fallacy. Despite their theoretical understanding to the contrary, people may believe that after a certain number of draws, they are "due" for a yellow cube.

Homework 25   Should I Go On?

1. Suppose there are two classes with 30 students in each class.

   In both classes, the students are individually playing Little Pig. In both classes, every student has gotten exactly 10 points so far in the current turn.

   In one class, each student draws just one more cube. In the other class, they all decide to stop at 10 points.

   a. For the class in which students all draw once more, how many would you expect to end up with 0 points? With 11 points? With 14 points? What would you expect for the total number of points in the class? What would you expect for the class average?

   b. Compare the expected class average from part a to the average for the class where everyone stopped at 10 points. Which class would you expect to have a better average?

2. Now suppose the situation is the same except that every student has only 2 points. Again, the students in the first class each draw just once more, while the students in the second class all stop at 2 points.

   a. What would you expect for the average score in the class where all the students draw once more?

   b. Which class would you expect to have a better average?

Homework 25:
Should I Go On?

This assignment focuses students' attention on the same type of comparison of one strategy with another that they have used in the past few days.

The Game of Pig

**Days
26–29**

Back To Pig

Ta-da! You're about to find the best strategy for Little Pig. Then all you will need to do is apply your new insights to the original game of Pig. Once you've done so, you'll be ready to wrap up this unit with portfolios, end-of-unit assessments, and work on *POW 7: Make A Game*.

***This page in the
student book
introduces Days 26
through 29***

***Anthony Pace, Geneva Fiore, Amy Jones, and Oscar Sharp try out their own
created games from "POW 7: Make a Game."***

The Best Little Pig

Students figure out the best strategy for Little Pig and return to Big Pig.

Mathematical Topics

- Finding the best strategy for Little Pig
- (Optional) Simulating Little Pig on a computer

Outline of the Day

In Class

1. Discuss *Homework 25: Should I Go On?*
   - Limit discussion to the specific cases in the assignment
   - Observe that deciding whether or not to go on depends only on the score at that point, and connect this to the gambler's fallacy
2. *The Best Little Pig*
   - Students find the Little Pig strategy with the maximum expected value
3. Discuss *The Best Little Pig*
   - Look first at cases where the initial score is not 5 points

- Realize that the 5-point and 6-point strategies are both optimal
4. (Optional) Simulate Little Pig on a computer
   - Confirm the theoretical analysis
5. Return to Big Pig
   - (Optional) Do an area analysis of the expected value for the 2-roll strategy

At Home

Homework 26: Big Pig Meets Little Pig

Special Materials Needed

- (Optional) A computer and software (such as the *IMP Pig* simulation Program) for a Little Pig simulation

Discuss With Your Colleagues

The General Analysis of Little Pig Strategies

The jump from area diagrams of individual strategies to the general analysis is a big one.

Is the mathematics of this transition clear to you? Is it clear to your students? Can students make the jump? What if some can and some can't?

1. Discussion of *Homework 25: Should I Go On?*

Although this is a routine expected value exercise, it develops an idea that is crucial in determining the best strategy for Little Pig (and similarly for Big Pig).

You can let one or two volunteers present their analysis of the homework situations. (*Note:* You should limit discussion to the specific cases in the assignment, since students will do the general analysis in today's activity, *The Best Little Pig.*)

In the class where students draw again, one would expect about ten students (out of 30) to draw a yellow cube and end up with 0 points, ten to draw red and end up with 11 points, and ten to draw blue and end up with 14 points.

This gives a total of 250 points, for an average of about 8.33 points per student, so this class ends up worse off (on the average) than the class where students stop at 10 points. *Caution:* Both classes end up with averages much higher than the

expected value for any of the Little Pig strategies that students have examined. That's because all the students in the problem start with 10 points. If a player starts at 0, it is unusual to get as high as 10 points.

A similar analysis for Question 2 shows that in the class where students draw again, students end up with an average score of 3 points (ten students get 0 points, ten get 3, and ten get 6), so students in this class are better off (on the average) than the students who stop at 2 points.

"What conclusions can you draw from this about Little Pig?"

Ask students what conclusion they can draw from Question 1 about Little Pig strategies. They should be able to articulate that if you reach 10 points, you will be better off *in the long run* if you stop rather than draw again.

Then ask students to state the implications of Question 2 for Little Pig strategies. They should be able to articulate that you will be better off *in the long run* if you draw again rather than stop if you have only 2 points.

• *Does it matter how they got there?*

"Does it matter how the students in the homework situation got to their score of 10 points?"

This is a good time to raise the issue of whether it matters how the individual students in Question 1 each got to their initial situations of having 10 points. (For example, they might have drawn ten red cubes, or two reds and two blues, and so forth.)

Students should be able to articulate that it doesn't make any difference, *as long as you assume that the next draw still has an equal chance of being yellow, red, or blue.* In other words, as long as you don't fall into the gambler's fallacy, the decision about whether or not to go on depends only on the number of points you have, and not on how you got to that score.

You may want to connect this point explicitly with the gambler's fallacy, so that students see the role of the activity *The Gambler's Fallacy* in the overall unit.

2. The Best Little Pig

(see next page)

At this point, students should be ready to make a final analysis of what the best strategy is for Little Pig.

If students are not sure how to proceed, you can suggest that they try some other cases between 2 and 10 points, using an analysis similar to that used for last night's homework.

You may want to have some groups prepare presentations for individual cases. If any group does an algebraic analysis you should have that group prepare a presentation as well.

3. Discussion of The Best Little Pig

Let diamond card students make presentations for groups that prepared individual cases. These presentations will probably be similar to those for *Homework 25: Should I Go On?* You may find it best to start with cases in which the initial score is not 5 points, and then come to that case later.

Students should see that for initial scores of less than 5 points, a player is better off drawing again, but with scores of more than 5 points, a player is better off stopping. If students analyze the specific case of 5 points, they will see that with exactly 5 points, it is equally good to stop or to draw once more.

In other words, the 5-point strategy and the 6-point strategy give the same expected value, and either one gives a larger expected value than any other strategy.

> *Note:* A supplemental problem, *Pig Strategies by Algebra,* asks students to find the expected value if a Little Pig player draws once more starting with S points, and then to determine what value of S makes drawing again worthwhile. The supplemental problem asks a similar question about Big Pig.

4. Optional: Computer Simulation of Little Pig

> *Note:* If time is short, you may want to skip or delay the computer simulation so that you can make the transition to Big Pig, as described in the section below headed "Back to Big Pig."

The Best Little Pig

You've seen that in the long run, a person with 2 points in Little Pig will do better by drawing again, while a person with 10 points should stop.

So what is the best strategy for Little Pig? For what scores does it pay to draw again and for what scores should you stop?

Based on your findings, what strategy will give the highest possible expected value per turn?

You can confirm the analysis of different strategies experimentally using a simulation of Little Pig (such as the *IMP Pig* simulation program, available on the publisher's World Wide Web site).

In doing so, you may want to begin with a simple Little Pig strategy for which students have done a complete expected value analysis, such as the 2-draw strategy. Be sure that students are reasonably confident of their analysis for this strategy.

Start with a relatively small number of games, for example, 100. Run a simulation of this size several times, so that students see that the results for the average score vary considerably.

Gradually increase the number of games, so students see that as the number of games grows, the results become more consistent. Fortunately, even a run of 100,000 games takes only about 20 to 30 seconds (using *IMP Pig* on a Macintosh®), and this should produce quite reliable results, definitely good enough to convince students that the program is doing what it should.

Once students believe in the program, let them try some other strategies. Students should see that both the 5-point and the 6-point strategies give about the same results, close to the theoretical expected value of approximately 2.362. Runs of 100,000 games should be large enough to demonstrate that these two strategies give better results than anything else (although a 7-point strategy is close behind with an expected value of about 2.325).

The computer simulation should reinforce students' trust in the analysis of strategies they did earlier.

In addition to showing students how the technology allows simulation on a large scale, this simulation should reinforce a few general ideas about the use of simulations that may have already been discussed.

- Calculator (or computer) programs can be used to simulate probabilistic situations.

- The results of the simulation can be used to approximate probabilities when the probabilities are too difficult to calculate in other ways. (You can tell students that this is called the **Monte Carlo method.**)

- The results of the simulation can be used to confirm results obtained theoretically.

5. Back to Big Pig

Since students have been involved with Little Pig for several days, they may have lost sight of the fact that it was just a simplified version of the original game of Pig (also called Big Pig).

"What ideas can you apply to Big Pig from your work on Little Pig?"

Ask the class how they think they might use the lessons learned about Little Pig and apply them to Big Pig.

No major ideas are needed here, since mostly this discussion is just a transition to tonight's homework.

If anyone suggests doing area diagrams for Big Pig strategies, you might consider going through the 2-roll strategy for Big Pig.

The diagram below, similar to that for the 2-draw Little Pig strategy, may be helpful. (The numbers in the boxes show the points scored for a given sequence of rolls.) Students should be able to see that the expected value is $5\frac{5}{9} \approx 5.56$.

First roll

	1	2	3	4	5	6
1		0	0	0	0	0
2		4	5	6	7	8
3	0	5	6	7	8	9
4		6	7	8	9	10
5		7	8	9	10	11
6		8	9	10	11	12

Second roll

Perhaps after the discussion, let students vote on what they think the best strategy is. You can list the various candidates and the number of votes they get. If any students think they have good justifications for their answers, you can let them try to convince the class.

Homework 26:
Big Pig Meets
Little Pig
(see facing page)

This assignment is the Big Pig analogue of last night's assignment.

Homework 26   Big Pig Meets Little Pig

In *Homework 25: Should I Go On?*, you looked at the question of when a player should draw again in Little Pig.

Now, you will examine how to apply that approach to Big Pig (that is, to the original game of Pig).

Assume that there are two large classes of students, but this time all the students are playing Big Pig.

1. Suppose each student has a current score of 10 points. In one class, each student rolls one more time and then stops. In the other class, each student stops at 10 points.

    Which class would you expect to end up with the better average score?

2. Consider at least two other initial scores (instead of 10 points), and decide which class you would expect to be better off—the class where each student rolls once more, or the class in which all the students stop.

Solving the Unit Problem

Students find the best strategy for the game of Pig, thus solving the unit problem.

Mathematical Topics

- Comparison of Pig and Little Pig
- Finding the best strategy for Pig
- (Optional) Simulating Pig on a computer

Special Materials Needed

- (Optional) A computer and software (such as the *IMP Pig* simulation program) for a Pig simulation

Outline of the Day

In Class

1. Discuss *Homework 26: Big Pig Meets Little Pig*
   - Discuss the expected value analysis for several cases
   - Find the best strategy for Big Pig
2. (Optional) Simulate Pig on a computer

- Confirm the theoretical analysis

At Home

Homework 27: The Pig and I

Discuss With Your Colleagues

Pig and the Gambler's Fallacy

Many people initially think that the best strategy for Pig is to stop after a particular number of rolls. The analysis in the unit shows that, in fact, the best strategy is to stop after reaching a particular number of points.

How might this common initial misconception be connected with the gambler's fallacy? Why might this fallacy lead one to choose a "roll" strategy rather than a "points" strategy?

---

1. Discussion of *Homework 26: Big Pig Meets Little Pig*

Let students have a few minutes to compare results and then let heart card students make presentations for various cases.

> The basic idea here is identical to that in *Homework 25: Should I Go On?*, although the computations are more cumbersome.
>
> For example, if there are 30 students with 10 points each, and they each roll once more, then one would expect five students to end up with 12 points, five students to end up with 13 points, five students to end up with 14 points, five students to end up with 15 points, five students to end up with 16 points, and five students to end up with 0 points.
>
> This comes to a total of 350 points, for an average of 11.67 points per player.
>
> Students should see that, by this analysis, a player with 10 points is better off in the long run rolling again.

• *The best Pig strategy*

It is likely that some students will have found that the break-even point for Big Pig occurs when the students have 20 points. In other words, a player with less than 20 points is better off rolling again, a player with more than 20 points is better off stopping, and for a player with exactly 20 points, the two options are equally good.

If no one has reached this conclusion, have students continue to work until they find the score at which one should stop rolling. You can facilitate this effort by having different groups test different numbers.

Keep in mind that this analysis is the culmination of the entire unit's work. It answers the question posed at the beginning of the unit (on Day 2), so it should be given appropriate fanfare.

• *Summary*

In summary, if you want to maximize your expected value, you should roll again whenever your current score is less than 20 points, and you should stop whenever your current score is more than 20 points. If your current score is exactly 20 points, you do equally well rolling or stopping.

In other words, the 20-point strategy and the 21-point strategy give the same expected value, and they are both better than any other strategy.

Note: Although this analysis shows what the best strategy is, it does not tell students what the expected value is for that strategy. An approach similar to that for Little Pig is extremely complicated and not very practical. It is possible to show by alternative methods, however, that the expected value for both the 20-point strategy and the 21-point strategy is approximately 8.142.

• Roll-based strategies

As discussed earlier, the best possible strategy for either Little Pig or Big Pig is one in which the decision about whether to draw or roll again is based on the number of points you have.

However, students may be interested in other strategies, and specifically may want to know how the point-based strategies compare to roll-based strategies (that is, strategies in which you stop after a specific number of rolls).

It can be shown that an *n*-roll strategy (for Big Pig) has a theoretical expected value of

$$\left(\frac{5}{6}\right)^n \cdot 4n$$

For whole numbers, this expression is maximized for $n = 5$ and $n = 6$, which give identical results that are approximately 8.038.

An equivalent to roll-based strategies is explored in the supplemental activity *Fast Pig*.

2. Optional: Computer Simulation of Big Pig

Finally, you can test the various strategies for Big Pig by using a simulation, such as *IMP Pig*.

Using 200,000 or more games should be enough to indicate that the best strategy (of those that can be tested) is one in which you stop after *about* 20 points. It takes more games than you want to do to make a clear distinction as to *exactly* what the very best stopping point is. (It may amaze students how much variation there is from one run to the next, even when using hundreds of thousands of games in each run.)

You may want to try a large number of turns with both the 20-point and 21-point strategies. If time allows, try 19 or 22 points and see what happens. As noted above, the results will probably not seem definitive.

Note: Students may be interested in strategies that are neither "roll" nor "point" strategies, such as mixtures of the two. These cannot be tested on the *IMP Pig* simulation program.

Homework 27   The Pig and I

You've worked through Little Pig strategies and then gone back to study the original game of Pig.

Based on your experiences with both of these games, summarize what you have learned about the best possible strategy for Pig.

Be sure to include what you think is the best strategy, how you found it, how you can justify that choice, and what you learned about "roll" strategies and "point" strategies.

Homework 27: The Pig and I

This homework gives students an opportunity to synthesize their work on Pig.

DAY 28

Game Workday

Students work on POW 7.

Mathematical Topics

- Using probability in the context of student-created games

Outline of the Day

In Class

1. Discuss *Homework 27: The Pig and I*

2. Students work on *POW 7: Make a Game*

At Home

Homework 28: Beginning Portfolio Selection

1. Discussion of *Homework 27: The Pig and I*

Use your judgment about whether a discussion is needed on this assignment. You may want to have a few students read their summary comments, or you may just collect them and later post some of the best essays.

2. POW 7 Workday

The balance of this day is set aside for students to work in pairs on *POW 7: Make a Game*. You may also want to plan for students to get some time to see what their classmates are doing.

You may want to remind students that when they turn in their final versions of these games, they must also turn in a written explanation of how they used ideas about probability and strategy in the game.

Homework 28

Beginning Portfolio Selection

This unit involved two main approaches for finding probabilities:

- simulations and experiments
- theoretical analyses—using rugs, area models, or tree diagrams

Select an activity from the unit that represents each approach.

Explain what each activity was about and describe what you learned about probability from it.

(This selection and explanation is the first step toward compiling your portfolio for this unit.)

Homework 28: Beginning Portfolio Selection

This assignment gets students started on compiling their portfolios for the unit and asks them to think about a specific aspect of the mathematics developed in the unit.

Portfolios

Students compile their portfolios for the unit.

Mathematical Topics

• Reviewing the unit and preparing unit portfolios

Outline of the Day

In Class

1. Remind students that unit assessments will take place tomorrow and tomorrow night

2. *"The Game of Pig" Portfolio*
   • Students write cover letters and assemble portfolios for the unit

At Home

Students complete portfolios and prepare for assessments

1. Reminder: Unit Assessments Tomorrow

Let students know that they will get their in-class and take-home unit assessments tomorrow. You may want to remind them to bring their notebooks to class tomorrow because the assessment is open book.

2. *"The Game of Pig" Portfolio*

Tell students to read over the instructions in *"The Game of Pig" Portfolio* carefully. Then they should take out all of their work for the unit.

They will have done part of the selection process in last night's homework, and their main task today is to write their cover letters. (If students have not yet completed the games, they can do the written work on them later.)

If students do not complete their cover letters, you may want them to take the materials home and finish compiling their portfolios for homework.

"The Game of Pig" Portfolio

As with *Patterns,* your portfolio for *The Game of Pig* has three parts.

- Writing a cover letter that summarizes the unit

- Choosing papers to include from your work in this unit

- Discussing your personal growth during the unit

Cover Letter for "The Game of Pig"

Look back over *The Game of Pig* and describe the central problem of the unit and the main mathematical ideas. This description should give an overview of how the key ideas were developed and how they were used to solve the central problem.

As part of the compilation of your portfolio, you will select some activities that you think were important in developing the key ideas of this unit. Your cover letter should include an explanation of why you are selecting each particular item.

Selecting Papers from "The Game of Pig"

Your portfolio for *The Game of Pig* should contain

- *Homework 27: The Pig and I*

- *Homework 28: Beginning Portfolio Selection*

  Include the two activities from the unit that you selected in *Homework 28: Beginning Portfolio Selection,* along with your written work about these activities that was part of the homework.

Continued on next page

Be sure that they bring the portfolio back tomorrow with the cover letter as the first item. They should also bring to class any other work that they think will be of help on tomorrow's unit assessments. The remainder of their work can be kept at home.

- *POW 7: Make a Game*

  Include your written explanation of how you used ideas about probability and strategy in your game, and any other written work you turned in during the development process. If possible, include the game itself.

- Other key activities

  Include two or three other activities that you think were important in developing the key ideas of this unit.

- Another Problem of the Week

  Select one of the first three POWs you completed during this unit (*A Sticky Gum Problem*, *What's on Back?*, or *Linear Nim*).

- Other quality work

  Select one or two other pieces of work that demonstrate your best efforts. (These can be any work from the unit—Problem of the Week, homework, classwork, presentation, and so forth.)

Personal Growth

Your cover letter for *The Game of Pig* describes how the mathematical ideas develop in the unit. As part of your portfolio, write about your own personal development during this unit. You may want to address this question:

> *How do you think the ideas in this unit might affect your own behavior in situations that involve probability?*

You should include here any other thoughts you might like to share with a reader of your portfolio.

Homework: Prepare for Assessments

Students' homework for tonight is to prepare for tomorrow's assessments by reviewing the ideas of the unit.

Students do the in-class assessment and can begin the take-home assessment.

Special Materials Needed

- *In-Class Assessment for "The Game of Pig"*
- *Take-Home Assessment for "The Game of Pig"*

• •

Outline of the Day

In Class

Introduce assessments

- Students do *In-Class Assessment for "The Game of Pig"*
- Students begin *Take-Home Assessment for "The Game of Pig"*

At Home

Students complete *Take-Home Assessment for "The Game of Pig"*

End-of-Unit Assessments

Note: The in-class portion of unit assessments is intentionally short so that time pressure will not be a factor in students' ability to do well. The IMP *Teaching Handbook* contains general information about the purpose of end-of-unit assessments and how to use them.

Tell students that today they will get two tests—one that they will finish in class and one that they can start in class and will be able to finish at home. The take-home part should be handed in tomorrow.

Tell students that they are allowed to use graphing calculators, notes from previous work, and so forth, when they do the assessments. (They will have to do without graphing calculators on the take-home portion unless they have their own.)

The assessments are provided separately in Appendix B for you to duplicate.

In-Class Assessment for "*The Game of Pig*"

Consider the following game.

In each turn of the game, you flip a coin three times. If you get three heads, you win 7 points. If you get the sequence "head, tail, head," you get 3 points.

If you get any other sequence, you get no points for that turn.

What is your expected value per turn for this game? Explain your reasoning.

Homework: Complete *Take-Home Assessment for* "*The Game of Pig*"

Students should bring back the completed assessment tomorrow. As with all work done at home, students may collaborate or get assistance, but they should report this as part of their write-up of the assessment.

• •

Take-Home Assessment for *The Game of Pig*

1. *Tetrahedron Dice*

Suppose you have two dice shaped like
tetrahedrons. (A tetrahedron is a solid
figure with four faces, as suggested in
the pictures to the right.)

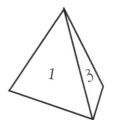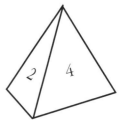

These dice each have the numbers
1, 2, 3, and 4 on them, one number on
each face. When one of these dice is
"rolled," each face is equally likely to end
up on the bottom. The number on the
bottom is considered the "result" when
you "roll" one of these dice.

Make up a game for two players in which the winner is determined by the sum of the
results from rolling this pair of dice. Create your game so that one player has a
probability of $\frac{5}{16}$ of winning and the other player has a probability of $\frac{11}{16}$ of winning.

Explain the rules clearly and explain how you know what each probability is.

2. *County Fair*

You are setting up a booth at the county fair. You will have a paper bag containing three
$10 bills, two $5 bills, and one $1 bill. Each contestant will draw two bills out of the bag.
If the contestant draws two $10 bills or two $5 bills, the contestant gets to keep the
bills. Otherwise, the contestant gets nothing.

If you charge $5 for each contestant, will you make money or lose money in the long
run? How much will you gain or lose on the average for each contestant? Explain your
answer.

DAY 31 *Summing Up*

Students sum up what they learned in the unit.

Mathematical Topics

• Summarizing the unit

Outline of the Day

In Class
1. Discuss unit assessments
2. Sum up the unit

Note: The discussion ideas below are written as if they take place on the day following the assessments, but you may prefer to delay presenting this material until after you have looked over students' work on the assessments.

1. Discussion of Unit Assessments

"Can anyone explain it a different way?"

You can have students volunteer to explain their work on each of the problems. Encourage questions and alternative explanations from other students.

• *In-Class Assessment*

Students should be able to see, by using a rug model or tree diagram, that the probability of getting three heads is $\frac{1}{8}$ and that the probability of getting the sequence "head, tail, head" is also $\frac{1}{8}$.

Using a set of, say, 800 turns, they should get a total of 1000 points, for an average score of 1.25 points per turn.

• *Take-Home Assessment*

Students will probably come up with a variety of games for Question 1. Use your judgment as to how many to discuss. You will probably want to discuss explicitly the probabilities for each possible two-dice sum.

The main step in Question 2 is finding the probability of drawing two $10 bills and the probability of drawing two $5 bills. Students will probably use one of the techniques discussed on Day 20 for *Homework 19: The*

Carrier's Payment Plan Quandary. (You need not review all the methods if students don't bring them up.)

Once they find these probabilities ($\frac{1}{5}$ for two \$10 bills, $\frac{1}{15}$ for two \$5 bills), they should be able to answer the question without much trouble.

One approach is to consider, say, 60 contestants. One would expect 12 contestants to draw two \$10 bills, and the booth loses \$15 for each of them, for a total of \$180 lost. Another 4 contestants draw two \$5 bills, and the booth loses \$5 for each of them, for a total of \$20 lost. For the remaining 44 customers, the booth gains \$5 each, for a total of \$220 gained.

Altogether, the booth gains \$20 from the 60 contestants, for an average gain of about 33¢ per contestant.

Another approach is to find the contestant's expected value (\$4.67) and then to subtract it from \$5 to get the booth's average gain.

In any case, students should conclude that in the long run, the booth should make money if it charges \$5 per person. They may point out that there are no guarantees about whether you win or lose, but that the more contestants you get, the more likely you are to make money.

They should also realize that the 33¢ gain is an average gain *per contestant*. To get the amount of money the booth expects to make, they should multiply 33¢ by the number of people that play.

2. Unit Summary

Let students share their portfolio cover letters as a way to start a discussion to summarize the unit.

"What have you learned in this unit?"

Then let them brainstorm to come up with statements about what they have learned in this unit. This is a good opportunity to review terms and to place the unit in a broader mathematics context.

The class may be aware that students in a traditional curriculum are busy learning algebra formulas and the like, and some may feel that they are missing out on something. Use this occasion to talk about the importance of probability in everyday life, and tell students that they will be working much more with probability over the four years of the IMP curriculum. You may also want to give them a glimpse of the kinds of statistics issues for which their knowledge of probability will be of help.

• •

Outline of the Day

In Class   Students share their POW 7 games

Discuss With Your Colleagues

Classroom Logistics of Game Day

**On Day 32, students will be displaying and sharing their games from
POW 7: Make a Game, and possibly trying to grade each other's games. This
is likely to lead to a somewhat chaotic classroom. A similar situation may
prevail on Day 28.**

**How can the logistics of activities like *POW 7: Make a Game* be handled as
smoothly as possible? Is there a danger of too much chaos? Is there a risk
of imposing too much structure in order to avoid chaos? What can you do
to increase your tolerance of classroom chaos?**

Sharing POW 7 Games

This day is set aside for students to display their final games and view each
other's games.

Whatever grading mechanism you are using can be put into operation today.

Appendix A — Supplemental Problems

The appendix contains a variety of activities that you can use to supplement the unit material. These activities are placed at the end of the student materials and fall roughly into two categories.

- Reinforcements, which are intended to increase students' understanding and comfort with concepts, techniques, and methods that are discussed in class and that are central to the unit

- Extensions, which allow students to explore ideas beyond the basic unit, and which sometimes deal with generalizations or abstractions of ideas that are part of the main unit

The supplemental activities are given here and in the student materials in the approximate sequence in which you might use them in the unit. The discussion below gives specific recommendations about how each activity might work within the unit.

For more ideas about the use of supplemental activities in the IMP curriculum, see the IMP *Teaching Handbook*.

• *Average Problems* (extension)

The problems in this activity are designed to strengthen students' intuition about how averages work (and don't work). Students will probably need to do some numerical experimentation to solve them. (The first problem is intended as a warm-up to get students going on the others.)

You can use this activity at any time, but students will be better motivated after a class discussion about averages (for example, after the Day 3 discussion of *Homework 2: Waiting for a Double*).

• *Mix and Match* (reinforcement)

Mix and Match provides additional opportunities for students to work with the basic definition of probability given on Day 5.

It involves counting the number of ways to create pairs by using one item from one set and one item from another set. It requires students to take into account the fact that different outcomes may not be equally likely. It might best be used as a follow-up to the discussion of Question 3 in *Homework 7: Portraits of Probability*.

- *Counters Revealed* (extension)

    This activity is a follow-up to *The Counters Game*, so it can be used at any time after Day 9. It offers students the opportunity to study a simplified version of that game. Students will probably do some experimental work on this activity, but they should also have reasoned explanations for their conclusions.

    Because of this problem's investigatory and open-ended nature, you may want to allow students up to a week to work on it.

- *Different Dice* (reinforcement)

    This activity looks at probabilities for various sums and products of two dice, but uses a pair of modified dice. It is similar to *Homework 11: Two-Dice Sums and Products*. It also brings out the idea that the sum of all the probabilities in a given situation has to equal 1.

- *Two-Spinner Sums* (extension or reinforcement)

    This activity is similar to *The Theory of Two-Dice Sums,* but has a slightly different setting. Question 2 asks students to compare the probabilities in these two situations, so this activity involves some new ideas.

- *Three-Dice Sums* (extension or reinforcement)

    Three-Dice Sums asks students to find the probability for different sums of three dice, and it can be used any time after Day 11.

- *Heads or Tails?* (extension)

    This activity is another example of the type of rug model used in the analysis of two-dice sums (Days 10 and 11) and can be used after Day 11.

    The activity begins with a review of the analysis that was done on Day 8 for Question 3 of *Homework 7: Portraits of Probability*. Students might approach Question 3b of *Heads or Tails* by seeing a pattern in the answers to Questions 1 and 2, rather than by a formal analysis.

    You may want to allow up to a week for students to work on this open-ended problem.

- *Expected Conjectures* and *Squaring the Die* (extensions)

    These two activities offer students opportunities to gain deeper insight into expected value.

    Expected Conjectures focuses on the idea that the answer obtained by using the "large number of trials" method is actually independent of the number of trials. Question 3 suggests the idea of multiplying each possible numerical outcome by its probability and adding the results to get the expected value.

    Squaring the Die explores the way that expected value behaves when events are combined. Students will probably be surprised by the result on Question 4.

    These activities can be used any time after Day 14, and you'll want to allow students substantial time to work on them.

• *Fair Spinners* (reinforcement)

> The first problem in this activity is similar to *Homework 14: A Fair Rug Game?*, except that it uses a spinner instead of a rug, and it is essentially the same as the "Spins" part of the activity *Spins and Draws* (Day 17). Question 2 of this activity allows students to be more creative.

• *A Fair Dice Game?* (reinforcement or extension)

> This activity requires students to use their knowledge about two-dice sums as well as the concept of a fair game, so it is a bit more difficult than either *Homework 14: A Fair Rug Game?* or the supplemental problem *Fair Spinners*.

• *Free Throw Sammy* (reinforcement)

> This is a routine follow-up to *The Theory of One-and-One* and can be used after Day 16. (It is slightly simpler than *Homework 16: Streak-Shooting Shelly*.)

• *Get a Head!* (extension)

> *Get a Head!* gives students a chance to combine some nontrivial probability with the concept of expected value. This activity can be used after about Day 18, so that students will already have had several experiences with expected value.

> Question 2 will require students to make a decision about dealing with arbitrarily long games. One way they might deal with this is to assume that the chances of a student getting, say, more than 15 heads is so small that they can ignore it. Another approach is to round off the number of events of each possible length. This will allow the student to ignore outcomes with very small probabilities.

• *Piling Up Apples* (extension)

> This is another strategy problem. It involves a variant of Nim in which one removes objects from one of several piles. It can be used as a follow-up to *POW 6: Linear Nim*, and so you can assign it after the POW presentations on Day 18.

• *Paying the Carrier* (extension)

> *Paying the Carrier* has a somewhat different flavor from the other carrier problems. It essentially requires students to develop and solve a linear equation (which might look like $30x + 6 \cdot 20 = 36 \cdot 5$), and then to generalize the result. You can use this activity at any point after the discussion of *Homework 19: The Carrier's Payment Plan Quandary*.

• *More Martian Basketball* (extension)

> This problem is a complex variation on the one-and-one-and-one problem in *Martian Basketball*, and it can be used any time after the discussion of *Martian Basketball* on Day 20.

> The choice of which player to pick may depend on how many points the team is ahead or behind. Lufy Boz is the player with the highest expected

value. But if the team is behind by three points, then Crago Dit is the one most likely to be able to tie the game. And if they want to maximize the chance of getting at least two points, then Splurge Ripo would be the best choice.

Because this problem involves several cases, students should be given several days to work on it.

- *Interruptions* (extension)

    The main problem in this activity is a much simplified version of the central problem of a Year 3 unit called *Pennant Fever*. Students can use simulations to get an idea of what's happening, but they should also be able to do an area diagram analysis similar to that used in analyzing Little Pig strategies.

    A general solution to this problem is too complex to expect at this stage, but students should be able to analyze other specific examples. This problem would be appropriate after Day 22, by which time students will have had several experiences using tree diagrams, and you may want to allow up to a week for students to work on it.

- *Pig Strategies by Algebra* (extension)

    This problem asks students to develop a general formula based on the reasoning in *Homework 25: Should I Go On?* and *Homework 26: Big Pig Meets Little Pig,* and can be assigned any time after Day 27.

- *Fast Pig* (extension)

    This activity uses a variant of the game of Pig in order to lead students toward a general analysis of the expected value for an n-roll strategy for Pig (see the subsection "Roll-based strategies" on Day 27). You may want to give students up to a week to do this problem.

Appendix *Supplemental Problems*

This page in the student book introduces the supplemental problems.

Probability, expected value, and the use of strategies are three of the important themes in *The Game of Pig*. The supplemental problems for this unit continue these themes. These are some examples:

- *Different Dice, Three-Dice Sums*, and *Heads or Tails?* ask you to find the probabilities for some events involving dice and coins.

- *Expected Conjectures* and *Squaring the Die* offer you a chance to get further insight into how expected value works.

- *Counters Revealed* and *Piling Up Apples* involve strategy for the counters game (from the activity of that name) and for a new game involving picking apples from piles.

Average Problems

1. Lucinda bought a dozen eggs on three different occasions. The average cost per dozen was $1.18.

   Give several different possible combinations for what the costs might have been for the different purchases.

Continued on next page

2. Two classes took an exam. In the first class, the average score was exactly 78%. In the second class, the average score was exactly 86%. But when the two classes were treated as one large group, the average was not 82%.

   a. How is this possible?

   b. What's the highest that the combined average could be? What's the lowest?

   c. Under what circumstances would the average of the two class averages be the same as the average you get when you treat the two classes as one large group? Explain your answer and be as complete as you can.

   Be sure to justify your answers.

3. Garrison Keillor describes Lake Wobegon as a place where "the children are all above average."

   Suppose someone measured all 85 ten-year-olds in the town and found that their average height was 4 feet 7 inches.

   a. Is it possible that all the ten-year-olds are taller than 4 feet 7 inches?

   b. If not, what is the largest number of ten-year-olds who could be taller than that? Explain your answer.

   c. Is it possible that Garrison Keillor is right, and all the ten-year-olds in Lake Wobegon are taller than average? What could that mean?

Mix and Match

Glenn likes to wear gloves. But he has some funny habits about his gloves. He keeps all of the left-hand gloves in one drawer and all of the right-hand gloves in another.

When he gets ready to go out on a cold day, he just pulls out one glove at random from each drawer and puts them on, without checking to see if they match.

Right now his left-hand glove drawer has two brown gloves and three gray gloves. His right-hand glove drawer has one brown glove, two gray gloves, and two red gloves. (Glenn also loses a lot of gloves.)

1. What is the probability that he will pull out a pair of gray gloves today?

2. What is the probability that he will pull out a matching pair of gloves today?

3. What is the probability that neither of his gloves will be brown?

Counters Revealed

Here is a simplified version of the counters game.

As in the regular version, your board consists of a rectangle with squares numbered from 2 through 12.

2	3	4	5	6	7	8	9	10	11	12

But instead of 11 counters to place on the board, you have only 2. You can place them in the same square if you want, or you can place them in two different squares.

As before, a pair of dice is rolled on each turn, and the numbers are added. If you have a counter in the square that matches the sum, you can remove that counter (but only one counter per roll). Your goal is to remove your counters as quickly as possible.

The challenge is to decide where to place the two counters to make your chances of winning quickly as good as possible.

1. Decide on at least three ways of placing the counters that you want to test out.

2. Set up a game board for one of your choices.

3. Play the game, and see how long it takes to win. Keep repeating until you think you have a good idea of how many rolls it would take, on average, to win with that placement of the counters.

4. Now repeat steps 2 and 3 for each of your other choices of initial position.

5. Write a report describing your work and summarizing your results. State any conclusions you reached, explaining your conclusions as well as you can.

Different Dice

Imagine a set of dice in which every 4 was replaced by a 7. So each die could roll 1, 2, 3, 5, 6, or 7, with each result equally likely.

Find the probability of each of the following results when rolling two of these dice.

1. The sum of the dice is 7.

2. The sum of the dice is less than 7.

3. The sum of the dice is greater than 7.

4. The product of the dice is even.

5. The product of the dice is odd.

6. Both dice are the same.

7. The sum of the dice is a multiple of 3.

8. The product of the dice is a multiple of 3.

Two-Spinner Sums

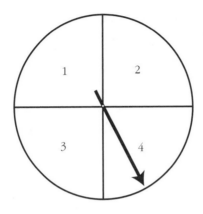 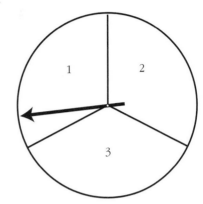

In some board games, you move your marker a certain number of spaces based on the result of a spinner.

Suppose you were playing a game using the two spinners above.

The rule is that you spin each spinner and move the same number of spaces as the sum of the two results.

1. Suppose you need a total of at least 5 from the two spinners to reach the winning position on the board. What is your probability of success?

2. Consider the various possible two-spin sums and the probabilities for each. How do these results compare to the results for two-dice sums? What are the similarities and what are the differences?

Three-Dice Sums

Suppose you roll three standard dice and add up the results. The lowest sum you can get is 3 (by rolling three 1's), and the highest is 18 (by rolling three 6's).

1. Without doing any analysis, what sums would you expect to be the most likely? Why?

2. Find the probability of getting each of the possible three-dice sums. Describe any patterns that you find, and explain them if you can.

3. Make up and answer some questions about three-dice sums.

Heads or Tails?

Coin #1

	H	T
H	Both heads	Tails on coin #1; heads on coin #2
T	Heads on coin #1; tails on coin #2	Both tails

Coin #2

You know that if you toss a balanced coin many times, you should get heads about half the time, and tails about half the time.

If you toss two balanced coins, the diagram at the left shows that the probability that they would both come out heads is $\frac{1}{4}$.

For example, if 100 people each tossed a pair of coins, about 25 of them would get two heads. Similarly, about 25 would get two tails, and about 50 would get one head and one tail.

1. Do a similar analysis for the case of three coins. That is, suppose three coins are all tossed at once, and find each of these probabilities.

    a. The probability of getting heads for all three coins

    b. The probability of getting two heads and one tail

    c. The probability of getting one head and two tails

    d. The probability of getting tails for all three coins

2. Now do the case of four coins. (*Hint:* Begin by making a list of the possible results.)

3. If there were ten coins, what would be the probability of getting

    a. all heads?

    b. nine heads and one tail?

4. What generalizations can you make about your results?

Expected Conjectures

Al and Betty were getting used to the idea of expected value, and they were making some conjectures.

Al wanted to find the expected value if you roll a die. He imagined rolling 600 times and figured that he would get about 100 one's, 100 two's, and so on.

So he did this computation:

$$100 \cdot 1 + 100 \cdot 2 + \cdots + 100 \cdot 6$$

This gave a total of 2100 points for the 600 rolls. He then divided by 600 to get the average per roll, which came out to 3.5.

1. Betty tried it with 6000 rolls and got the same average. Explain why their averages are the same. (Look for more than one explanation.)

2. When Al saw that the average was the same both ways, he decided he could find the average with only six rolls. Would he still get the same result? Explain.

3. Could you find the average with only one roll? Explain.

Squaring the Die

Here are some more conjectures that Al and Betty are making about expected value. What do you think of their ideas?

Use the definition of expected value based on "the long run" to justify your evaluation of their conjectures.

1. Al says: If you roll a die, the expected value is 3.5, since results of 1 through 6 are equally likely, and 3.5 is the average of the numbers 1, 2, 3, 4, 5, and 6.

   Does this give the right answer? Explain.

2. Betty says: If you roll two dice, the expected value should be twice as big as if you roll one die. Based on Al's idea in Question 1, she thinks the expected value for a two-dice sum is 7.

   What do you think? Explain.

Continued on next page

3. Al says: If the expected value for the *sum* of two dice is 3.5 + 3.5, then the expected value for the *product* of two dice should be 3.5 · 3.5, which is 12.25.

   Is Al right? Explain.

4. Finally, Betty says: If you roll a die and square the number that shows, the expected value for the result should be the square of the expected value for a single die, that is, 3.5^2, which is 12.25.

   Is Betty right? Explain.

Fair Spinners

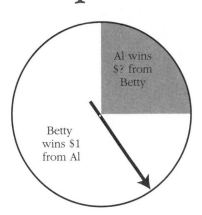

1. Al and Betty are interested in changing their spinner game so that neither player has an advantage.

   They decide to use the same spinner that you saw in *Spinner Give and Take*, but they want to modify the game by changing the amount that Al wins when the spinner lands on the gray area.

   In other words, Betty still wins $1 from Al when the spinner lands in the white section. But Al wins some other amount when the spinner lands in the gray section.

   What should the new amount be so that the game is fair? Explain how you arrived at your answer.

2. Make up and solve a spinner problem of your own.

A Fair Dice Game?

Here's a game to consider.

We throw a pair of dice. If the sum is 2, 11, or 12, you win. If the sum is 7, I win. If the sum is anything else, no one wins, and we throw again. We keep throwing until one of us wins.

1. Do you think this game is fair? In other words, are we each equally likely to win? Explain why or why not. Use a rug (or rugs) in your explanation.

2. If you think it *is* a fair game, make up another dice game that you think *is not* fair. If you think the game *is not* fair, make up another dice game that you think *is* fair. Once again, use a rug in your explanation.

Free Throw Sammy

Sammy has a free throw success rate of 80%.

Construct an area model for the one-and-one situation with Sammy.

1. Using your area model, what is the probability that Sammy will get

    a. zero points?

    b. one point?

    c. two points?

2. Use your area model to find Sammy's expected value per one-and-one situation.

Get a Head!

At a school fund-raiser, students set up a booth with this game:

> You start flipping a regular coin. Each time you get heads, you get a payoff of $1. If you get tails, the game ends, and you get to keep the money you've won so far. (If you get tails on your first flip, you get nothing.)
>
> Also, if you get ten straight heads, you get your $10, but the game ends and you are given a $50 bonus.

For example, if you flip four heads and then tails, you win $4. If you flip ten heads, you win $60 altogether.

1. If the school charges $2 to play and each of the 1000 students at the school plays five times, how much profit should the school expect to make altogether?

2. The students are considering eliminating both the limit of ten heads and the bonus. How much profit should they expect to get if they make these changes? (*Note:* You may need to give an approximate answer to this problem, and you should definitely explain your reasoning.)

Piling Up Apples

Once upon a time, Al and Betty were collecting apples. They had collected two piles and were bored. So they decided to play a game.

They would take turns taking some apples from one of the piles. The one who took the last apple would win. They decided on these rules.

- On any turn, a player must take at least one apple.

- On any turn, a player can take apples from only one of the piles.

Continued on next page

At first, they decided to go alphabetically, so that Al would always choose first. At the end of each game, they would put the piles back the way they originally were.

There were 11 apples in Pile A and 8 apples in Pile B. After a few games, Al found a strategy so that he always won.

1. Figure out Al's strategy, and explain how he could always win.

The next day they played the same game, except the piles they played with were not the same size as the day before. Al still insisted on going first, but now, no matter what he did, Betty always won.

2. Figure out how many apples might have been in each pile, so that Betty could always beat Al, and explain how she won.

Each morning after that, they would decide what size piles they were going to use for that day. On each day, either Al won every game or Betty won every game. (Al still always went first.)

3. a. Find a rule, in terms of the sizes of the piles, that explains which player will always win.

   b. For the sizes where Al always wins, explain what his strategy is.

   c. For the sizes where Betty always wins, explain what her strategy is.

Eventually, they decided to switch to playing the game with three piles. Al still always went first, and they kept the same rules:

   • On any turn, a player must take at least one apple.

   • On any turn, a player can only take apples from one of the piles.

They found that with three piles, it was harder to tell who would win.

4. Find three piles so that Al can always win, and explain how he should play with these piles to insure a win.

5. Find three piles so that Betty can always win, and explain how she should play with those piles to insure a win.

Paying the Carrier

Now, you are the customer. Instead of paying $5 weekly, you decide to offer your newspaper carrier a different payment method.

The carrier will roll a pair of dice. If the sum is 4 or less, the carrier will get $20. If the sum is more than 4, the carrier will get some other fixed amount.

1. What should you choose for the other fixed amount (that is, the amount that the carrier gets for anything over 4) in order for this payment method to be equivalent, in the long run, to the $5 per week payment?

2. Describe in words how you found the answer in Question 1.

3. Now suppose that the normal weekly cost of the paper was $Y but the carrier still gets $20 for a sum of 4 or less. What should you choose for the other fixed amount that the carrier gets (for any sum over 4) in order to make the payoff fair in the long run? (*Hint:* Work with some specific values for Y.)

More Martian Basketball

You may recall from the activity *Martian Basketball* that instead of having one-and-one free throw situations, Martians have one-and-one-and-one situations.

Here is information on three of the Martian Basketball Association All-Star players.

- Splurge Ripo: a 70% shooter in any situation

- Crago Dit: makes 70% of first shots, 60% of second shots, and 90% of third shots

- Lufy Boz: makes 80% of first shots, 50% of second shots, and 90% of third shots

Suppose the Martian All-Stars were playing the team from Venus, and for the last play of the game, the Martians got to choose one of their players for a one-and-one-and-one situation. Who would be the best person to have shooting? Who would be the worst? How might it depend on the score at that point?

Write an analysis of different cases and how you would decide each one.

Interruptions

Al and Betty are at the park flipping coins. Al gets a point if the coin is heads, and Betty gets a point if the coin is tails.

The first one to reach 10 points wins a prize of $15.

But with Al leading by a score of 8 to 7, Al's parents and Betty's parents interrupt the game, and Al and Betty are told that they each have to go home. They decide that, rather than hope to finish the game another time, they should just give out the prize now.

Al says, since he was leading, he should get the prize. Betty figures that each point should be worth $1, so Al should get $8 and she should get $7.

One of the parents suggests that they should figure out the probability each had of winning, and divide the money according to that.

1. How should they divide the money if they take this parent's advice? Explain your results carefully.

2. Pick two other possible incomplete games, and figure out how Al and Betty should divide the money using the parent's system.

Pig Strategies by Algebra

In *Homework 25: Should I Go On?* and in *Homework 26: Big Pig Meets Little Pig,* you looked at the question of when it pays for a player of Little Pig or Big Pig to draw or roll again.

In those assignments, you assumed that a group of students each had a particular score, and you found the expected value if they each drew or rolled once more.

In this assignment, you should work more generally.

1. Assume that a player has exactly *S* points in Little Pig. Find an algebraic expression in terms of *S* for that player's expected value if the player decides to draw one more cube and then stop.

2. a. For what values of *S* is your expression from Question 1 greater than *S*? In other words, when does the player gain in the long run by drawing again?

   b. For what values of *S* is your expression from Question 1 less than *S*?

3. Now do the analogous questions for Big Pig. That is, suppose a player has *S* points in Big Pig.

   a. Find an algebraic expression in terms of *S* for that player's expected value if the player decides to roll the die one more time and then stop.

   b. For what values of *S* is your expression from Question 3a greater than *S*? In other words, when does the player gain in the long run by rolling again?

   c. For what values of *S* is your expression from Question 3a less than *S*?

Interactive Mathematics Program 185

Fast Pig

Fast Pig is another variation of the game of Pig.

Instead of rolling one die again and again, you roll several dice at once, and you get only one roll per turn. (That's what makes it fast.)

If none of the dice comes up 1, your score is the sum of the dice. But if one or more of the dice comes up 1, your score for the turn is 0.

Although Fast Pig with just one die isn't very exciting, you may want to think about that game to get some ideas about the questions below.

1. Suppose you play Fast Pig with two dice.

   a. What is the probability that neither die will be a 1?

   b. If you consider only those turns with a non-zero score, what is your expected value for a turn of Fast Pig? (You might imagine dice with only five sides, labeled 2 through 6.)

   c. Taking into account your answers to parts a and b, what is the expected value altogether for a turn of two-dice Fast Pig?

2. Answer the same questions for three-dice Fast Pig.

3. Can you generalize the results? (You may want to think about one-die Fast Pig as well.)

4. What does the analysis of *n*-dice Fast Pig tell you about the expected value for certain strategies for Pig?

Appendix B

Blackline Masters

For discussion of *Rug Games* on Day 7, you will find it helpful to have overhead transparencies of the diagrams. This appendix contains copies of these diagrams for your use in making such transparencies. You will probably want to use these transparancies again in the discussion of *Homework 12: Pointed Rugs.*

This appendix also contains copies of the in-class and take-home assessments for the unit.

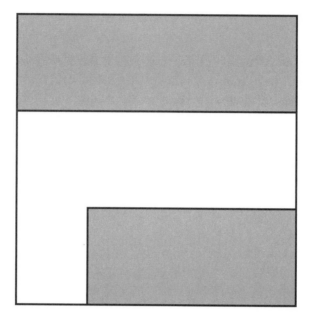

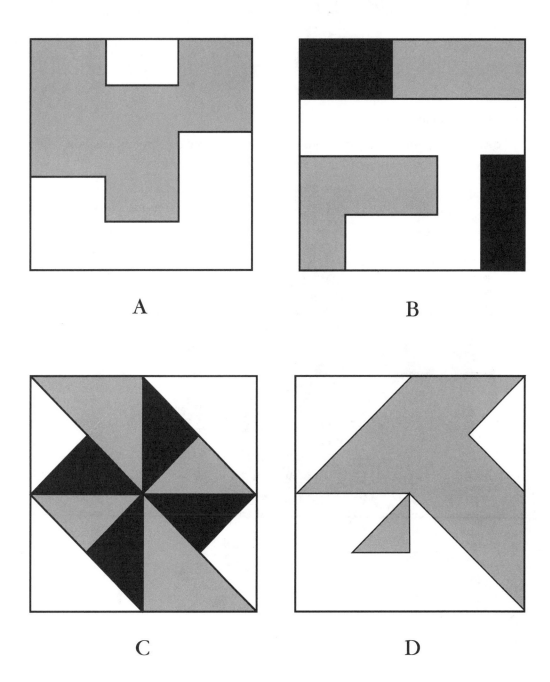

A   B

C   D

In-Class Assessment for "The Game of Pig"

Consider the following game.

In each turn of the game, you flip a coin three times. If you get three heads, you win 7 points. If you get the sequence "head, tail, head," you get 3 points.

If you get any other sequence, you get no points for that turn.

What is your expected value per turn for this game? Explain your reasoning.

Take-Home Assessment for *The Game of Pig*

1. *Tetrahedron Dice*

Suppose you have two dice shaped like tetrahedrons. (A tetrahedron is a solid figure with four faces, as suggested in the pictures to the right.)

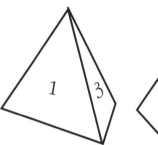 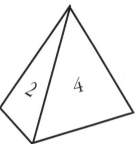

These dice each have the numbers 1, 2, 3, and 4 on them, one number on each face. When one of these dice is "rolled," each face is equally likely to end up on the bottom. The number on the bottom is considered the "result" when you "roll" one of these dice.

Make up a game for two players in which the winner is determined by the sum of the results from rolling this pair of dice. Create your game so that one player has a probability of $\frac{5}{16}$ of winning and the other player has a probability of $\frac{11}{16}$ of winning.

Explain the rules clearly and explain how you know what each probability is.

2. *County Fair*

You are setting up a booth at the county fair. You will have a paper bag containing three $10 bills, two $5 bills, and one $1 bill. Each contestant will draw two bills out of the bag. If the contestant draws two $10 bills or two $5 bills, the contestant gets to keep the bills. Otherwise, the contestant gets nothing.

If you charge $5 for each contestant, will you make money or lose money in the long run? How much will you gain or lose on the average for each contestant? Explain your answer.

Glossary

This is the glossary for all five units of IMP Year 1.

Absolute value   The distance a number is from 0 on the number line. The symbol | | stands for absolute value.

Examples: $|-2| = 2$; $|7| = 7$; $|0| = 0$

Acute angle   An angle that measures more than 0° and less than 90°.

Acute triangle   A triangle whose angles are all acute.

Adjacent angles   Two angles with the same vertex and formed using a shared ray.

Example: Angles A and B are adjacent angles.

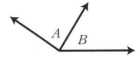

Adjacent side   (for an acute angle of a right triangle) The side of the right triangle which, together with the hypotenuse, forms the given angle.

Example: In the right triangle ABC, side $\overline{BC}$ is adjacent to $\angle C$, and side $\overline{AB}$ is adjacent to $\angle A$.

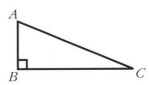

Alternate interior angles   If two lines are intersected by a transversal, then the inside angles that are on opposite sides of the transversal are alternate interior angles.

Example: Angles *K* and *L* are one pair of alternate interior angles, and angles *M* and *N* are another pair.

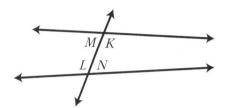

Amplitude

(for a pendulum) The angle of a pendulum's swing, measured from the vertical to the most outward position of the pendulum during its swing.

Example: The pendulum in the diagram has an amplitude of 20°.

Angle

Informally, an amount of turn, usually measured in **degrees.** Formally, the geometric figure formed by two **rays** with a common initial point, called the **vertex** of the angle.

Angle of elevation

The angle at which an object appears above the horizontal, as measured from a chosen point.

Example: The diagram shows the angle of elevation to the top of the tree from point *A*.

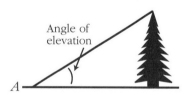

Area

Informally, the amount of space inside a two-dimensional figure, usually measured in square units.

Area model

For probability, a diagram showing the possible outcomes of a particular event. Each portion of the model represents an outcome, and the ratio of the area of that portion to the area of the whole model is the probability of that outcome.

Axis (plural: **axes**) See **Coordinate system.**

Coefficient Usually, a number being used to multiply a variable or power of a variable in an algebraic expression.

Example: In the expression $3x + 4x^2$, 3 and 4 are coefficients.

Complementary angles A pair of angles whose measures add to 90°. If two complementary angles are adjacent, together they form a right angle.

Composite number A counting number having more than two whole-number divisors.

Example: 12 is a composite number because it has the divisors 1, 2, 3, 4, 6, and 12.

Conclusion Informally, any statement arrived at by reasoning or through examples.

See also **"If . . . , then . . ." statement.**

Conditional probability The probability that an event will occur based on the assumption that some other event has already occurred.

Congruent Informally, having the same shape and size. Formally, two polygons are congruent if their corresponding angles have equal measure and their corresponding sides are equal in length. The symbol $\cong$ means "is congruent to."

Conjecture A theory or an idea about how something works, usually based on examples.

Constraint Informally, a limitation or restriction.

Continuous graph Informally, a graph that can be drawn without lifting the pencil, in contrast to a **discrete graph.**

Coordinate system A way to represent points in the plane with pairs of numbers called **coordinates**. The system is based on two perpendicular lines, one horizontal and one vertical, called **coordinate axes.** The point where the lines meet is called the **origin.** Traditionally, the axes are labeled with the variables x and y as shown below. The horizontal axis is often called the **x-axis** and the vertical axis is often called the **y-axis.**

Example: Point A has coordinates $(3, -2)$.

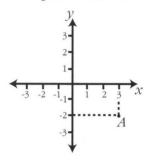

Corresponding angles

(for a transversal) If two lines are intersected by a transversal, then two angles are corresponding angles if they occupy the same position relative to the transversal and the other lines that form them.

Example: Angles A and D are a pair of corresponding angles, and angles B and E are another pair of corresponding angles.

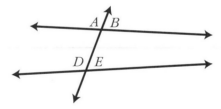

Corresponding parts

For a pair of similar or congruent polygons, sides or angles of the two polygons that have the same relative position.

Example: Side a in the small triangle and side b in the large triangle are corresponding parts.

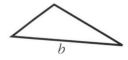

Counterexample	An example which demonstrates that a conjecture is not true.
Degree	The measurement unit for an angle defined by having a complete turn equal to 360 degrees. The symbol ° represents degrees.
Diagonal	In a polygon, a line segment that connects two vertices and that is not a side of the polygon.
Discrete graph	A graph consisting of isolated or unconnected points, in contrast to a **continuous graph.**
Divisor	A factor of an integer.
	Example: 1, 2, 3, 4, 6, and 12 are the positive divisors of 12.
Domain	The set of values that can be used as inputs for a given function.
Equilateral triangle	A triangle with all sides the same length.
Expected value	In a game or other probability situation, the average amount gained or lost per turn in the long run.
Exterior angle	An angle formed outside a polygon by extending one of its sides.
	Example: The diagram shows an exterior angle for polygon *ABCDE*.

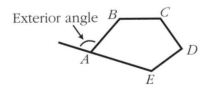

Factor	The same as **divisor.**
Factorial	The product of all the whole numbers from a particular number down to 1. The symbol ! stands for factorial.
	Example: 5! (read "five factorial") means 5 · 4 · 3 · 2 · 1.
Fair game	A game in which both players are expected to come out equally well in the long run.

Frequency bar graph	A bar graph showing how often each result occurs.

Example: This frequency bar graph shows, for instance, that 11 times in 80 rolls, the sum of two dice was 6. |

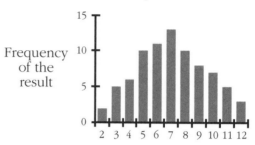

Function	Informally, a process or rule for determining the numerical value of one variable in terms of another. A function is often represented as a set of number pairs in which the second number is determined by the first, according to the function rule.
Graph	A mathematical diagram for displaying information.
Hexagon	A polygon with six sides.
Hypotenuse	The longest side in a right triangle, or the length of this side. The hypotenuse is located opposite the right angle.

Example: In right triangle *ABC*, the hypotenuse is $\overline{AC}$. |

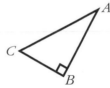

Hypothesis	Informally, a theory about a situation or about how a certain set of data is behaving. Also, a set of assumptions being used to analyze or understand a situation.

See also **"If . . . , then . . ." statement.** |
| *"If . . . , then . . ." statement* | A specific form of mathematical statement, saying that if one condition is true, then another condition must also be true.

Example: Here is a true "If . . . , then . . ." statement.

If two angles of a triangle have equal measure, then the sides opposite these angles have equal length. |

The condition "two angles of a triangle have equal measure" is the **hypothesis.** The condition "the sides opposite these angles have equal length" is the **conclusion.**

Independent events

Two (or more) events are independent if the outcome of one does not influence the outcome of the other.

Integer

Any number that is either a counting number, zero, or the opposite of a counting number. The integers can be represented using set notation as

$$\{ \ldots -3, -2, -1, 0, 1, 2, 3, \ldots \}.$$

Examples: $-4, 0,$ and 10 are integers.

Interior angle

An angle inside a figure, especially within a polygon.

Example: Angle *BAE* is an interior angle of the polygon *ABCDE*.

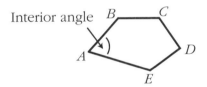

Isosceles triangle

A triangle with two sides of equal length.

Leg

Either of the two shorter sides in a right triangle. The two legs of a right triangle form the right angle of the triangle. The longest side of a right triangle (the hypotenuse) is not considered a leg.

Line of best fit

Informally, the line that comes closest to fitting a given set of points on a discrete graph.

Line segment

The portion of a straight line between two given points.

Mathematical model

A mathematical description or structure used to represent how a real-life situation works.

Mean

The numerical average of a data set, found by adding the data items and dividing by the number of items in the set.

Example: For the data set 8, 12, 12, 13, and 17, the sum of the data items is 62 and there are 5 items in the data set, so the mean is 62 ÷ 5, or 12.4.

Measurement variation   The situation of taking several measurements of the same thing and getting different results.

Median   (of a set of data) The "middle number" in a set of data that has been arranged from smallest to largest.

Example: For the data set 4, 17, 22, 56, and 100, the median is 22, because it is the number in the middle of the list.

Mode   (of a set of data) The number that occurs most often in a set of data. Many sets of data do not have a single mode.

Example: For the data set 3, 4, 7, 16, 18, 18, and 23, the mode is 18.

Natural number   Any of the counting numbers 1, 2, 3, 4, and so on.

Normal distribution   A certain precisely defined set of probabilities, which can often be used to approximate real-life events. Sometimes used to refer to any data set whose frequency bar graph is approximately "bell-shaped."

Observed probability   The likelihood of a certain event happening based on observed results, as distinct from **theoretical probability.**

Obtuse angle   An angle that measures more than 90° and less than 180°.

Obtuse triangle   A triangle with an obtuse angle.

Octagon   An eight-sided polygon.

Opposite side   The side of a triangle across from a given angle.

Order of operations   A set of conventions that mathematicians have agreed to use whenever a calculation involves more than one operation.

Example: 2 + 3 · 4 is 14, not 20, because the conventions for order of operations tell us to multiply before we add.

Ordered pair	Two numbers paired together using the format *(x, y)*, often used to locate a point in the coordinate system.
Origin	See **Coordinate system.**
Parallel lines	Two lines in a plane that do not intersect.
Pentagon	A five-sided polygon.
Perimeter	The boundary of a polygon, or the total length of this boundary.
Period	The length of time for a cyclical event to complete one full cycle.
Perpendicular lines	A pair of lines that form a right angle.
Polygon	A closed two-dimensional shape formed by three or more line segments. The line segments that form a polygon are called its sides. The endpoints of these segments are called **vertices** (singular: **vertex**).

Examples: All the figures below are polygons.

Prime number	A whole number greater than 1 that has only two whole number divisors, 1 and itself.

Example: 7 is a prime number, because its only whole number divisors are 1 and 7.

Probability	The likelihood of a certain event happening. For a situation involving equally likely outcomes, the probability that the outcome of an event will be an outcome within a given set is defined by a ratio:

$$\text{Probability} = \frac{\text{number of outcomes in the set}}{\text{total number of possible outcomes}}$$

Example: If a die has 2 red faces and 4 green faces, the probability of getting a green face is

$$\frac{\text{number of green faces}}{\text{total number of faces}} = \frac{4}{6}$$

Proof   An absolutely convincing argument.

Proportion   A statement that two ratios are equal.

Proportional   Having the same ratio.

Example: Corresponding sides of triangles *ABC* and *DEF* are proportional, because the ratios $\frac{4}{6}$, $\frac{8}{12}$, and $\frac{10}{15}$ are equal.

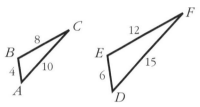

Quadrant   One of the four areas created in a coordinate system by using the *x*-axis and the *y*-axis as boundaries. The quadrants have standard numbering as shown below.

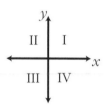

Quadrilateral   A four-sided polygon.

Random   Used in probability to indicate that any of several events is equally likely or that an event is selected from a set of events according to a precisely described distribution.

Range   (of a set of data) The difference between the largest and smallest numbers in the set.

Example: For the data set 7, 12, 18, 18, and 29, the range is 29 – 7, or 22.

Ray   The part of a line from a single point, called the **vertex,** through another point on the line and continuing infinitely in that direction.

Rectangle	A four-sided polygon whose angles are all right angles.
Regular polygon	A polygon whose sides all have equal length and whose angles all have equal measure.
Rhombus	A four-sided polygon whose sides all have the same length.
Right angle	An angle that measures 90°.
Right triangle	A triangle with a right angle.
Sample standard deviation	The calculation on a set of data taken from a larger population of data, used to estimate the standard deviation of the larger population.
Sequence	A list of numbers or expressions, usually following a pattern or rule. Example: 1, 3, 5, 7, 9, . . . is the sequence of positive odd numbers.
Similar	Informally, having the same shape. Formally, two polygons are similar if their corresponding angles have equal measure and their corresponding sides are proportional in length. The symbol ~ means "is similar to."
Simulation	An experiment or set of experiments using a model of a certain event that is based on the same probabilities as the real event. Simulations allow people to estimate the likelihood of an event when it is impractical to experiment with the real event.
Slope	Informally, the steepness of a line.
Solution	A number that, when substituted for a variable in an equation, makes the equation a true statement. Example: The value $x = 3$ is a solution to the equation $2x = 6$ because $2 \cdot 3 = 6$.
Square	A four-sided polygon with all sides of equal length and with four right angles.

Square root   A number whose square is a given number. The symbol $\sqrt{}$ is used to denote the nonnegative square root of a number.

                       Example: Both 6 and –6 are square roots of 36, because $6^2 = 36$ and $(-6)^2 = 36$; $\sqrt{36} = 6$.

*Standard
deviation*   A specific measurement of how spread out a set of data is, usually represented by the lowercase Greek letter sigma (σ).

Straight angle   An angle that measures 180°. The rays forming a straight angle together make up a straight line.

Strategy   A complete plan about how to proceed in a game or problem situation. A strategy for a game should tell a person exactly what to do under any situation that can arise in the game.

*Supplementary
angles*   A pair of angles whose measures add to 180°. If two supplementary angles are adjacent, together they form a straight angle.

Term   (of an algebraic expression) A part of an algebraic expression, combined with other terms using addition or subtraction.

                       Example: The expression $2x^2 + 3x - 12$ has three terms: $2x^2$, $3x$, and 12.

Term   (of a sequence) One of the items listed in a sequence.

                       Example: In the sequence 3, 5, 7, . . . , the number 3 is the first term, 5 is the second term, and so on.

*Theoretical
probability*   The likelihood of an event occurring, as explained by a theory or model, as distinct from **observed probability.**

Transversal   A line that intersects two or more other lines.

Example: The line *l* is a transversal that intersects the lines *m* and *n*.

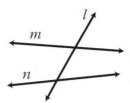

Trapezoid A four-sided polygon with exactly one pair of parallel sides.

Example: Quadrilateral *PQRS* is a trapezoid, because $\overline{QR}$ and $\overline{PS}$ are parallel and $\overline{PQ}$ and $\overline{SR}$ are not parallel.

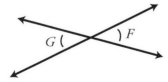

Triangle A polygon with three sides.

Triangle inequality principle The principle that the lengths of any two sides of a triangle must add up to more than the length of the third side.

Trigonometric function Any of six functions defined for acute angles in terms of ratios of sides of a right triangle.

Vertex (plural: **vertices**) See **Angle, Polygon,** and **Ray.**

Vertical angles A pair of "opposite" angles formed by a pair of intersecting lines.

Example: Angles *F* and *G* are vertical angles.

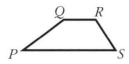

Whole number A number that is either zero or a counting number.

x-intercept A place on a graph where a line or curve crosses the *x*-axis.

y-intercept A place on a graph where a line or curve crosses the *y*-axis.

Photographic Credits

Teacher Book Classroom Photography

23 Shasta High School, Dave Robathan; **51** East Bakersfield High School, Susan Lloyd; **102** East Bakersfield High School, Susan Lloyd; **111** Napa High School, Lynne Alper; **169** East Bakersfield High School, Susan Lloyd

Student Book Classroom Photography

3 Lincoln High School, Lori Green; **14** Lincoln High School, Lori Green; **27** Lincoln High School, Lori Green; **36** Lincoln High School, Lori Green; **42** San Lorenzo Valley High School, Kim Gough; **55** Lincoln High School, Lori Green; **95** Foothill High School, Cheryl Dozier; **104** Foothill High School,Cheryl Dozier; **114** Mendocino Community High School, Lynne Alper; **127** Mendocino High School, Lynne Alper; **150** Lake View High School, Carol Caref; **157** West High School, Janice Bussey; **189** Whitney Young High School, Carol Berland; **210** Pleasant Valley High School, Michael Christensen; **222** Lynne Alper; **238** East Bakersfield High School, Susan Lloyd; **252** Lincoln High School, Lynne Alper; **274** Colton High School, Sharon Taylor; **281** Foothill High School, Cheryl Dozier; **307** Santa Cruz High School, Lynne Alper; **324** Foothill High School, Cheryl Dozier; **352** Santa Maria High School, Mike Bryant; **366** Santa Cruz High School, Lynne Alper; **373** Shasta High School, Dave Robathan; **397** Santa Cruz High School, Lynne Alper; **414** Santa Maria High School, Mike Bryant; **424** Bartram Communications Academy, Robert Powlen; **446** Santa Maria High School, Mike Bryant; **460** Ranum High School, Rita Quintana

Student Book Classroom Photography

Katrina Van Loan, Jenee Desmond, David Trammel, Gina Uriarte, Thea Singleton, Itan Novis, Sarah N. Weintraub (photographed by Hillary Turner at Tamalpais High School)